curriculum mathematics practice 3

C Oliver   **A Ledsham**   **R Elvin**   **M Bindley**

Oxford University Press

Oxford University Press, Great Clarendon Street, Oxford OX2 6DP

Oxford   New York
Athens   Auckland   Bangkok   Bogotá   Buenos Aires
Calcutta   Cape Town   Chennai   Dar es Salaam
Delhi   Florence   Hong Kong   Istanbul   Karachi
Kuala Lumpur   Madrid   Melbourne   Mexico City
Mumbai   Nairobi   Paris   São Paulo   Shanghai
Singapore   Taipei   Tokyo   Toronto   Warsaw

and associated companies in

Berlin   Ibadan

Oxford is a trade mark of Oxford University Press
© Oxford University Press 1996

Series first published as *Comprehensive Mathematics Practice* 1981
Updated edition of *Curriculum Mathematics Practice* first published 1996
Reprinted 1997, 1998, 1999, 2000

ISBN 0 19 833743 4
A CIP record for this book is available from the British Library.

Typeset and illustrated by Tech Set Ltd
Printed and bound in Great Britain by Butler and Tanner Ltd, Frome and London

Preface

Curriculum Mathematics Practice is an updated version of *Comprehensive Mathematics Practice*, a successful series designed for the majority of students in their first years of secondary schooling. As before, the books provide a vast range of carefully constructed and graded exercises in a coherent mathematical progression, with many of these exercises set in a real-life context. The levels targeted are 3–8, and details of how all six new books relate to the curriculum are given in the Answer Book.

These new books do not attempt to provide a complete scheme for the National Curriculum. No attempt has been made for instance to cover 'Using and Applying Mathematics' or computer work. It is expected, however, that mathematics departments will use other resources for those aspects (e.g. *Oxford Mathematics*) and that *Curriculum Mathematics Practice* will provide a core of skill practice within an overall scheme of work.

The series has the same objective as the original books. The series should enable students 'to gain confidence in their abilities and master the fundamental processes so necessary for future success'.

Mark Bindley
Revising Editor
December 1995

Contents

Unit 1 Negative numbers

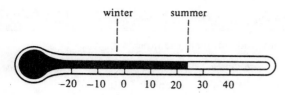

On the Celsius temperature scale, the freezing point of water is 0 °C.

The temperature on a summer's day might be 23°, written as +23 °C.

The temperature on a frosty day in winter might be 2° below zero, written as −2 °C.

Normally the temperature is above 0 °C, so only those temperatures below the freezing point need a sign.

Thus, body temperature is 37 °C; the temperature inside a freezer is −3 °C. This is a negative temperature, read as minus 3 °C.

Example 1

The temperature is 10 °C.

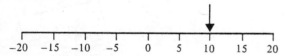

Find the new temperature if

a the temperature rises by 5°
b the temperature falls by 5°

a New temperature $= 10 + 5 = 15$ °C
b New temperature $= 10 - 5 = 5$ °C

Example 2

The temperature is 0 °C.

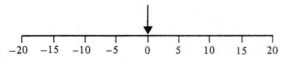

Find the new temperature if

a the temperature rises by 5°
b the temperature falls by 5°

a New temperature $= 0 + 5 = 5$ °C
b New temperature $= 0 - 5 = -5$ °C

Example 3

The temperature is −5 °C.

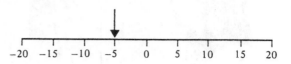

Find the new temperature if

a the temperature rises by 5°
b the temperature falls by 5°

a New temperature $= -5 + 5 = 0$ °C
b New temperature $= -5 - 5 = -10$ °C

Exercise 1.1

Copy and complete the table.

	temperature	change	new temperature
1	10 °C	rise 5°	
2	13 °C	+6°	
3	11 °C	+4°	
4	15 °C	fall 3°	
5	18 °C	−5°	
6	17 °C	−6°	
7	9 °C		11 °C
8	14 °C		10 °C
9	12 °C		5 °C
10		+5°	13 °C
11		−6°	5 °C
12	0 °C	fall 6°	
13	5 °C	fall 7°	
14	3 °C	−4°	
15	4 °C		−2 °C
16	0 °C		−5 °C
17		−3°	−1 °C
18		−8°	−3 °C
19	−3 °C	rise 7°	
20	−5 °C	+8°	
21	−4 °C		5 °C
22	−3 °C		3 °C
23		+8°	6 °C
24		+9°	8 °C
25	−2 °C	fall 5°	
26	−5 °C	−4°	
27	−4 °C		−6 °C
28	−1 °C		−7 °C
29		−5°	−8 °C
30		−3°	−7 °C

2

The amount of money that is in your bank account is called the *balance*.

Taking money out of your account is called *making a withdrawal*.

Paying money into your account is called *making a deposit*.

Writing a cheque to pay for something is equivalent to making a withdrawal.

If you withdraw more money than is in your account, your account is *overdrawn* and you owe the bank money.

Example 4

a Ms Jones has a balance of £230 in her bank account.
If she writes a cheque for £350, how much is she overdrawn?

£350 is £120 more than £230, so Ms Jones has −£120 in her account. She is £120 *overdrawn*.

b Mr Smith was £455 overdrawn but then made a deposit of £600.
What is his new balance?

Mr Smith's balance before he paid in the £600 was −£455. £600 is £145 more than £455, so Mr Smith's new balance is £145.

Exercise 1.2

Copy and complete the table.

	balance	change	new balance
1	£340	deposit £400	
2	£235	deposit £1675	
3	£389	withdraw £350	
4	£1745	withdraw £705	
5	£3450	cheque £2775	
6	£209	cheque £209	
7	−£400	deposit £500	
8	−£783	deposit £800	
9	−£1000	deposit £1200	
10	−£275	deposit £645	
11	£500	withdraw £650	
12	£456	withdraw £457	
13	£371	withdraw £567	
14	−£300	deposit £200	
15	−£150	deposit £80	
16	−£321	deposit £212	
17	−£765	deposit £89	
18	−£200	withdraw £200	
19	−£47	cheque £56	
20	−£913	cheque £274	

Some calculators can deal with negative numbers. Those which can have a button like this

The button is used to enter the sign of a number. It is used after the number. So to enter −6 you press these buttons

6   +/−

The display will show

-6

To enter −8 + −14 you press

Example 5

Copy and complete the table.

number entered	calculation entered	answer displayed
8	+14	
8	−14	
−8	+14	
−8	−14	

number entered	calculation entered	answer displayed
8	+14	22
8	−14	-6
−8	+14	6
−8	−14	-22

Example 6

Copy and complete the table.

add	3	2	1	0	−1	−2	−3
2	5	4	3				
1							
0	3	2	1	0	−1	−2	−3
−1	2	1	0	−1			
−2							
−3							

Here is the completed table.

add	3	2	1	0	−1	−2	−3	
2	5	4	3	2	1	0	−1	a
1	4	3	2	1	0	−1	−2	
0	3	2	1	0	−1	−2	−3	
−1	2	1	0	−1	−2	−3	−4	b
−2	1	0	−1	−2	−3	−4	−5	c
−3	0	−1	−2	−3	−4	−5	−6	d

Exercise 1.3

Copy and complete the table.

	number entered	calculation entered	answer displayed
1	2	+3	
2	2	−3	
3	−2	+3	
4	−2	−3	
5	3	+2	
6	3	−2	
7	−3	+2	
8	−3	−2	
9	9	+11	
10	9	−11	
11	−9	+11	
12	−9	−11	
13	9	+5	
14	9	−5	
15	−9	+5	
16	−9	−5	
17	1	+1	
18	1	−1	
19	−1	+1	
20	−1	−1	

Exercise 1.4

Copy and complete the following tables.

1

add	6	4	2	0	−2	−4	−6
4	10	8	6				
2							
0							
−2	4	2	0	−2			
−4							
−6							

2

add	9	6	3	0	−3	−6	−9
6							−3
3	12						
0					−3		
−3							−12
−6	3						
−9				−6			

3

add	5	3	2	0	−2	−3	−5
2	7						
0		3					
−2			0				
−3				−3			
−5					−7		
−7						−10	

Look at the answer to Example 6 on page 3.

From line **a**

2 add 3 = 2 + 3 = 5

From line **b**

−1 add −1 = −1 + −1 = −2

From line **c**

−2 add −3 = −2 + −3 = −5

When the signs are the same, the sum also has the same sign.

Example 7

Add the following.

a −4 and −5 **b** −2, −3 and −4 **c** $-3x$ and $-4x$

a −4 + −5 = −9

b −2 + −3 + −4 = −5 + −4 = −9

c $-3x + -4x = -7x$

Exercise 1.5

For each of the following, add the numbers together.

1 3 and 5 **2** 2 and 13
3 5 and 11 **4** −3 and −5
5 −5 and −9 **6** −1 and −3
7 −2 and −13 **8** −5 and −5
9 −2, −4 and −5 **10** −2, −5 and −7
11 −3, −5 and −8 **12** −1, −2 and −4
13 −1, −6 and −8 **14** $-2x$ and $-4x$
15 $-3y$ and $-8y$ **16** $-4z$ and $-4z$
17 $-a$ and $-5a$ **18** $-2b$, $-5b$ and $-6b$
19 $-3c$, $-4c$ and $-7c$ **20** $-d$, $-4d$ and $-8d$

Look again at the answer to Example 6 on page 3.

From line **a**

2 add −3 = 2 + −3 = −1

From line **d**

−3 add 1 = −3 + 1 = −2

From line **c**

−2 add 3 = −2 + 3 = 1

When the signs are *not* the same, take the smaller number from the greater. Then write down the difference, together with the sign of the greater number.

Example 8

Add the following.

a −8 and 5 **b** 7 and −2 **c** $-6x$ and $8x$

a −8 + 5 = −3 **b** 7 + −2 = 5 **c** $-6x + 8x = 2x$

Exercise 1.6

For each of the following, add the numbers together.

1 −2 + 8 **2** −5 + 9 **3** −6 + 11
4 −1 + 16 **5** $-3x + 7x$ **6** $-4y + 12y$
7 $-z + 9z$ **8** 7 + −3 **9** 9 + −7
10 12 + −6 **11** $8a + -2a$ **12** $11b + -7b$
13 $15c + -12c$ **14** −8 + 5 **15** −9 + 3
16 −12 + 4 **17** −7 + 1 **18** $-6p + 2p$
19 $-10q + 3q$ **20** $-5r + 4r$ **21** 3 + −5
22 4 + −9 **23** 5 + −12 **24** $6u + -10u$

Example 9

Copy and complete the table.

take → / from ↓	4	3	2	1	0	−1	−2
10	6		8		10	11	
5					5	6	
0				−1	0	1	
−5					−5	−4	

Here is the completed table.

take → / from ↓	4	3	2	1	0	−1	−2	
10	6	7	8	9	10	11	12	**a**
5	1	2	3	4	5	6	7	
0	−4	−3	−2	−1	0	1	2	
−5	−9	−8	−7	−6	−5	−4	−3	**b**

Exercise 1.7

Copy and complete the following tables.

1

take → / from ↓	4	3	2	1	0	−1	−2
6	2	3			6	7	
3	−1					4	
0						1	
−3					−3	−2	

2

take → / from ↓	6	4	2	0	-2	-4	-6
12	6	8		12	14		
6	0			6	8		
0	-6						
-6	-12			-6	-4		

3

take → / from ↓	12	9	6	3	0	-3	-6
12		3				15	
6	-6					9	
0						3	
-6	-18					-3	

4

take → / from ↓	4	3	2	1	0	-1	-2
4							
0							
-4	-8					-3	
-8							

5

take → / from ↓	4	3	2	1	0	-1	-2
2	-2						
0							
-2							
-4							

6

take → / from ↓	15	10	5	0	-5	-10	-15
10							
5							
0							
-5							

Look at the answer to Example 9.

From line **a**
'from 10 take 3' $= 10 - 3 = 7$

From line **b**
'from -5 take 4' $= -5 - 4 = -9$

To subtract a positive number, simply take it away.

Example 10

Work out the following.

a 6 take 4 **b** 6 take 8 **c** -10a take 5a

a 6 take 4 is
$6 - 4 = 2$

b 6 take 8 is
$6 - 8 = -2$

c -10a take 5a is
$-10a - 5a = -15a$

Exercise 1.8

Work out each of the following.

1 10 take away 6
2 12 take away 5
3 11x take away 9x
4 7y take away y
5 5 take away 7
6 3 take away 8
7 4z take away 9z
8 8t take away 14t
9 u take away 3u
10 6v take away 7v
11 -3 take away 2
12 -9 take away 6
13 -7 take away 7
14 -8p take away 3p
15 -6q take away 4q
16 -2 take away 7
17 -8 take away 9
18 -5a take away 8a
19 -4b take away 11b
20 -c take away 15c

Look again at the answer to Example 9.

From line **a**
'from 10 take -2' $= 10 - -2$
$= 10 + 2$
$= 12$

From line **b**
'from -5 take -1' $= -5 - -1$
$= -5 + 1$
$= -4$

Subtracting a negative number is the same as adding it.

Exercise 1.9

Work out each of the following.

1 5 take away -2
2 8 take away -4
3 8x take away -3x
4 7y take away -5y
5 3 take away -7
6 2 take away -13
7 4z take away -6z
8 6t take away -12t
9 -2 take away -6
10 -4 take away -5
11 -6 take away -9
12 -5 take away -12
13 -3a take away -8a
14 -7b take away -9b
15 -c take away -9c
16 -5d take away -6d
17 -5 take away -2
18 -7 take away -5
19 -9 take away -4
20 -8x take away -2x
21 -10y take away -4y
22 -12z take away -8z
23 -20t take away -15t
24 -5u take away -u
25 -9v take away -8v

Unit 2 Decimals

Adding and subtracting

Revise your knowledge of decimal addition and subtraction by trying these.

Exercise 2.1

Find the 'odd answer out' for the following.

1   **a** $31.75 + 20.34 + 12.53$
   b $27.88 + 12.23 + 24.41$
   c $39.16 + 10.24 + 15.12$

2   **a** $15.24 + 12.32 + 4.75$
   b $19.43 + 8.57 + 4.41$
   c $8.86 + 6.42 + 17.03$

3   **a** $23.8 + 18.58 + 12.27$
   b $16.6 + 24.64 + 13.51$
   c $21.9 + 22.3 + 10.45$

4   **a** $16.38 + 5.46 + 6.5$
   b $17.6 + 6.6 + 4.14$
   c $9.74 + 9.5 + 9$

5   **a** $15.63 + 9.85 + 0.28$
   b $18.3 + 7.19 + 0.37$
   c $21.38 + 3.9 + 0.58$

6   **a** $43.98 - 29.13$
   b $32.92 - 18.17$
   c $51.04 - 36.29$

7   **a** $19.94 - 4.48$
   b $18.25 - 2.79$
   c $23.82 - 8.46$

8   **a** $18.54 - 15.3$
   b $14.7 - 11.56$
   c $18 - 14.76$

9   **a** $7.66 - 4.3$
   b $12.96 - 9.7$
   c $10.16 - 6.9$

10   **a** $14.6 - 8.18$
   b $9.4 - 2.88$
   c $12 - 5.58$

Multiplying and dividing

Example 1

Find the value of the following.

A calculator can be used, or the calculations can be completed in the following way.

a 0.3×6 **b** 0.4×0.2

a 0.3×6
$$= 3 \div 10 \times 6$$
$$= 3 \times 6 \div 10$$
$$= 18 \div 10 = 1.8$$

b 0.4×0.2
$$= 4 \div 10 \times 2 \div 10$$
$$= 4 \times 2 \div 100$$
$$= 8 \div 100 = 0.08$$

Exercise 2.2

Find the value of the following.

1 0.2×7	**2** 0.4×8	**3** 0.9×6
4 1.6×8	**5** 2.3×5	**6** 3.2×8
7 0.45×3	**8** 0.24×7	**9** 0.47×6
10 0.07×9	**11** 0.08×5	**12** 0.04×2
13 0.8×0.3	**14** 0.7×0.6	**15** 0.6×0.5
16 0.15×0.6	**17** 0.24×0.8	**18** 0.33×0.5
19 0.04×0.2	**20** 0.02×0.3	**21** 0.05×0.3
22 1.3×0.5	**23** 1.6×0.4	**24** 1.3×0.7
25 4.8×0.4	**26** 3.6×0.5	**27** 1.24×0.3
28 1.92×0.2	**29** 1.04×0.6	**30** 1.32×0.5

Example 2

Find the value of the following.

A calculator can be used or the calculations can be completed in the following way.

a 2.6×1.3 **b** 6.8×0.21

a 2.6×1.3
$$= 26 \div 10 \times 13 \div 10$$
$$= 26 \times 13 \div 100$$
$$= 338 \div 100 = 3.38$$

$$\begin{array}{r} 26 \\ \times 13 \\ \hline 260 \\ 78 \\ \hline 338 \end{array}$$

b 6.8×0.21
$$= 68 \div 10 \times 21 \div 100$$
$$= 68 \times 21 \div 1000$$
$$= 1428 \div 1000 = 1.428$$

$$\begin{array}{r} 68 \\ \times 21 \\ \hline 1360 \\ 68 \\ \hline 1428 \end{array}$$

Exercise 2.3

Find the value of the following.

1 2.3×1.4	**2** 3.2×1.6	**3** 4.3×1.5
4 2.1×1.8	**5** 3.9×1.2	**6** 2.5×2.1
7 2.4×1.5	**8** 3.5×2.4	**9** 8.2×1.6
10 9.8×1.2	**11** 9.3×1.5	**12** 5.3×2.4
13 4.8×2.1	**14** 8.8×1.5	**15** 6.4×2.5
16 3.2×0.14	**17** 4.5×0.13	**18** 2.4×0.18
19 6.3×0.12	**20** 2.8×0.21	**21** 9.6×0.09
22 8.7×0.08	**23** 4.8×0.15	**24** 9.2×0.16

Example 3

Find the value of the following.

A calculator can be used or the calculations can be completed in the following way.

a $12.5 \div 5$ **b** $4.9 \div 7$ **c** $4 \div 5$

a
$$\begin{array}{r} 2.5 \\ 5\overline{)12.5} \\ \underline{10} \quad (5 \times 2) \\ 2.5 \\ \underline{2.5} \quad (5 \times 0.5) \end{array}$$

b $4.9 \div 7$
$$\begin{array}{r} 0.7 \\ 7\overline{)4.9} \\ \underline{4.9} \quad (7 \times 0.7) \end{array}$$

So $4.9 \div 7 = 0.7$

c $4 \div 5$

We must write 4 as 4.0.

$$\begin{array}{r} 0.8 \\ 5\overline{)4.0} \\ \underline{4.0} \quad (5 \times 0.8) \end{array}$$

So $4 \div 5 = 0.8$

Exercise 2.4

Find the value of the following.

1 $13.6 \div 4$	**2** $11.4 \div 3$	**3** $14.5 \div 5$
4 $15.6 \div 6$	**5** $27.2 \div 8$	**6** $26.4 \div 6$
7 $37.1 \div 7$	**8** $40.5 \div 9$	**9** $4.8 \div 3$
10 $3.4 \div 2$	**11** $5.2 \div 4$	**12** $8.7 \div 3$
13 $9.6 \div 4$	**14** $4.5 \div 5$	**15** $3.5 \div 7$
16 $3.2 \div 4$	**17** $5.6 \div 8$	**18** $3.6 \div 6$
19 $2.4 \div 3$	**20** $8.1 \div 9$	**21** $3 \div 5$
22 $4 \div 8$	**23** $6 \div 4$	**24** $8 \div 5$

Example 4

Find the value of the following.

A calculator can be used or the calculations can be completed in the following way.

a $1.25 \div 0.5$

Multiply the numerator and the denominator by 10 to make the divisor (0.5) a whole number.

$$1.25 \div 0.5 = \frac{1.25}{0.5}$$
$$= \frac{1.25 \times 10}{0.5 \times 10}$$
$$= \frac{12.5}{5}$$
$$= 2.5$$

$$\begin{array}{r} 2.5 \\ 5\overline{)12.5} \\ \underline{10} \\ 2.5 \\ \underline{2.5} \end{array}$$

b $0.036 \div 0.06$

Multiply the numerator and the denominator by 100 to make the divisor (0.06) a whole number.

$$0.036 \div 0.06 = \frac{0.036}{0.06}$$
$$= \frac{0.036 \times 100}{0.06 \times 100}$$
$$= \frac{3.6}{6}$$
$$= 0.6$$

$$\begin{array}{r} 0.6 \\ 6\overline{)3.6} \\ \underline{3.6} \end{array}$$

Exercise 2.5

Find the value of the following.

1 $5.28 \div 0.3$	**2** $7.25 \div 0.5$
3 $8.54 \div 0.7$	**4** $6.36 \div 0.6$
5 $8.05 \div 0.5$	**6** $7.2 \div 0.4$
7 $7.8 \div 0.3$	**8** $8.7 \div 0.6$
9 $9.6 \div 0.5$	**10** $1.34 \div 0.2$
11 $5.16 \div 0.6$	**12** $5.76 \div 0.8$
13 $3.44 \div 0.4$	**14** $0.78 \div 0.6$
15 $0.98 \div 0.7$	**16** $0.9 \div 0.5$
17 $0.6 \div 0.4$	**18** $0.85 \div 0.05$
19 $0.76 \div 0.02$	**20** $1.36 \div 0.04$
21 $2.52 \div 0.09$	**22** $2.8 \div 0.08$
23 $1.7 \div 0.05$	**24** $0.6 \div 0.03$
25 $0.052 \div 0.04$	**26** $0.072 \div 0.06$
27 $0.095 \div 0.05$	**28** $0.024 \div 0.03$
29 $0.035 \div 0.05$	**30** $0.072 \div 0.08$

Example 5

The price of printed cotton material is £5.24 per metre.

What is the price of a dress length of this material 2.5 m in length?

A calculator can be used or the calculation can be completed in the following way.

Price = £5.24 × 2.5

= £524 ÷ 100 × 25 ÷ 10

= £524 × 25 ÷ 1000

= £13 100 ÷ 1000 = £13.10

$$
\begin{array}{r}
524 \\
\times\ 25 \\
\hline
10\,480 \\
2\,620 \\
\hline
13\,100
\end{array}
$$

Exercise 2.6

1 Find the cost of carpeting a corridor of length 3.6 m if the price of the carpet is £7.50 per metre.
2 The weight of 1 metre of electric wiring is 0.06 kg. What is the weight of this wiring on a 50 metre reel?
3 The length and height of a section of fencing is shown below.

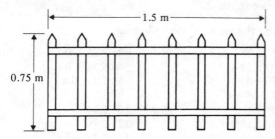

a Find the total length of wood required.
b The price of the wood is £1.20 per metre. What is the total cost of the wood?
4 Peter weighs 31.6 kg.
Find the weights of the following members of his family
a Peter's father who is 3 times heavier than Peter.

b Peter's mother who is 28.8 kg lighter than his father.
c His baby sister Jodie who weighs $\frac{1}{4}$ as much as his mother.

5 Wendy's folder contains 120 sheets of paper, each of weight 0.72 g.
If the empty folder weighs 113.6 g, what is the total weight of her folder and the paper?

6 A large thermos flask holds sufficient coffee to fill exactly 2 large cups of capacity 0.24 litres and 4 smaller ones of capacity 0.13 litres.
What is the capacity of the flask?

7 What is the length of each sausage in the string of sausages shown below?

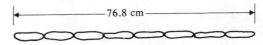

8 A pile of exercise books is 12 cm high.
If each book is 0.8 cm thick, how many are there in the pile?

9 How many pies can be made from 0.5 kg of flour if each pie requires 0.02 kg of the flour?

10 A bottle contains 0.9 litres of lemonade.
How many glasses, each of capacity 0.15 litres, can be filled from it?

11 A milkman is carrying a crate which contains 12 bottles and weighs 11.5 kg.
If the empty crate weighs 0.7 kg, what is the weight of each bottle of milk?

12 From the dimensions of the garage shown in the diagram below, find each of the following.
a The overall width of the garage.
b The height of the garage door.

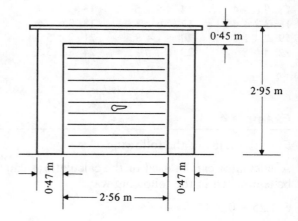

Exercise 2.7

Find the 'odd answer out' for the following.

1.   a 23.8×0.6
     b 36.7×0.4
     c 20.4×0.7

2.   a 72.8×0.5
     b 45.5×0.8
     c 36×0.9

3.   a 15.4×1.2
     b 11.3×1.6
     c 13.2×1.4

4.   a 12.9×1.5
     b 17.5×1.1
     c 7.7×2.5

5.   a 18.5×1.6
     b 19.6×1.5
     c 21×1.4

6.   a 10.5×1.5
     b 8.75×1.8
     c 9.85×1.6

7.   a $41.6 \div 0.8$
     b $37.1 \div 0.7$
     c $4.77 \div 0.09$

8.   a $14.4 \div 0.4$
     b $18 \div 0.5$
     c $21 \div 0.6$

9.   a $19.2 \div 1.2$
     b $28.8 \div 1.6$
     c $22.4 \div 1.4$

10.   a $71.4 \div 2.1$
      b $63 \div 1.8$
      c $51 \div 1.5$

11.   a $1.65 \div 0.11$
      b $3.84 \div 0.24$
      c $0.192 \div 0.012$

12.   a $2.1 \div 0.15$
      b $2.4 \div 0.16$
      c $0.35 \div 0.025$

13.   a $1.56 \div 1.2$
      b $1.95 \div 1.5$
      c $1.82 \div 1.3$

14.   a $2.88 \div 1.8$
      b $3.6 \div 2.4$
      c $4 \div 2.5$

15.   a $0.276 \div 1.2$
      b $0.504 \div 2.1$
      c $0.36 \div 1.5$

16.   a $0.84 \div 2.4$
      b $0.98 \div 2.8$
      c $0.9 \div 2.5$

Example 5

Given that $10.8 \times 7.8 = 84.24$, write down the answer to

a 108×7.8 **b** 108×78

a   108 is 10.8×10, and 7.8 is 7.8×1.
So the new product is (10×1) or 10 times bigger

$$84.24 \times 10 = 842.4$$

b   108 is 10.8×10, and 78 is 7.8×10.
So the new product is (10×10) or 100 times bigger

$$84.24 \times 100 = 8424$$

Example 6

Given that $27 \times 36 = 972$, write down the answer to

a 2.7×3.6 **b** 0.27×0.36

a   2.7 is 10 times smaller than 27, and 3.6 is 10 times smaller than 36.
So the new product is (10×10) or 100 times smaller

$$972 \div 100 = 9.72$$

b   0.27 is 100 times smaller than 27, and 0.36 is 100 times smaller than 36.
So the new product is (100×100) or 10 000 times smaller

$$972 \div 10\,000 = 0.0972$$

Exercise 2.8

1. Given that $5.4 \times 3.2 = 17.28$, write down the answer to
     a 54×3.2 **b** 5.4×32 **c** 54×32

2. Given that $2.4 \times 1.8 = 4.32$, write down the answer to
     a 24×1.8 **b** 2.4×18 **c** 24×18

3. Given that $3.5 \times 1.4 = 4.9$, write down the answer to
     a 35×1.4 **b** 3.5×14 **c** 35×14

4. Given that $3.6 \times 2.5 = 9$, write down the answer to
     a 36×2.5 **b** 3.6×25 **c** 36×25

5. Given that $0.57 \times 0.34 = 0.1938$, write down the answer to
     a 57×0.34 **b** 0.57×34 **c** 57×34

6. Given that $0.21 \times 0.16 = 0.0336$, write down the answer to
     a 21×0.16 **b** 0.21×16 **c** 21×16

7. Given that $0.72 \times 0.25 = 0.18$, write down the answer to
     a 72×0.25 **b** 0.72×25 **c** 72×25

8. Given that $0.48 \times 0.27 = 0.1296$, write down the answer to
     a 4.8×0.27 **b** 0.48×2.7 **c** 4.8×2.7

9. Given that $0.23 \times 1.2 = 0.0276$, write down the answer to
     a 2.3×0.12 **b** 0.23×1.2 **c** 2.3×1.2
     d 23×0.12 **e** 0.23×12 **f** 23×12

10 Given that $0.36 \times 0.15 = 0.054$, write down the answer to

a 3.6×0.15 **b** 0.36×1.5 **c** 3.6×1.5
d 36×0.15 **e** 0.36×15 **f** 36×15

Decimal places

A fraction is turned into a decimal by dividing the numerator by the denominator.

e.g. $\frac{3}{4} = 3 \div 4 = 0.75$

Example 7

Change

a $\frac{5}{8}$ into a decimal fraction

b $\frac{3}{40}$ into a decimal fraction

a $\frac{5}{8} = 5 \div 8$

$= 0.625$

$$
\begin{array}{r}
0.625 \\
8\overline{)5.000} \\
4\,8 \\
\hline
20 \\
16 \\
\hline
40 \\
40 \\
\hline
\end{array}
$$

b $\frac{3}{40} = 3 \div 40$

$= 0.075$

$$
\begin{array}{r}
0.075 \\
40\overline{)3.000} \\
2\,80 \\
\hline
200 \\
200 \\
\hline
\end{array}
$$

Exercise 2.9

Change the following into decimal fractions.

1 $\frac{3}{8}$ **2** $\frac{3}{10}$ **3** $\frac{7}{10}$ **4** $\frac{2}{5}$

5 $\frac{4}{5}$ **6** $\frac{9}{20}$ **7** $\frac{11}{20}$ **8** $\frac{9}{40}$

9 $\frac{17}{40}$ **10** $\frac{7}{40}$ **11** $\frac{1}{40}$ **12** $\frac{11}{50}$

13 $\frac{41}{50}$ **14** $\frac{5}{16}$ **15** $\frac{9}{16}$

Sometimes the equivalent decimal fraction is a recurring decimal, i.e. a decimal in which a figure or group of figures appears repeatedly.

e.g. $\frac{5}{9} = 0.555 \ldots$ or $0.\dot{5}$

$\frac{4}{11} = 0.3636\ldots$ or $0.\dot{3}\dot{6}$

Exercise 2.10

Change the following into decimal fractions.

1 $\frac{2}{3}$ **2** $\frac{1}{3}$ **3** $\frac{5}{6}$ **4** $\frac{1}{6}$

5 $\frac{5}{12}$ **6** $\frac{7}{12}$ **7** $\frac{11}{12}$ **8** $\frac{1}{12}$

9 $\frac{4}{9}$ **10** $\frac{7}{9}$ **11** $\frac{1}{9}$ **12** $\frac{6}{11}$

13 $\frac{3}{11}$ **14** $\frac{7}{30}$ **15** $\frac{13}{30}$

Decimal numbers and quantities are often approximated.

Example 8

a £1.26 is nearer to £1.30 than it is to £1.20; so £1.26 = £1.30 *to the nearest ten pence.*

b £1.62 is nearer to £2 than it is to £1; so £1.62 = £2 *to the nearest pound.*

Example 9

Give £16.35

a to the nearest ten pence
b to the nearest pound
c to the nearest ten pounds.

a 35 p is halfway between 30 p and 40 p, so it is rounded up;
so £16.35 = £16.40 to the nearest ten pence.

b £16.35 is nearer to £16 than it is to £17; so £16.35 = £16 to the nearest pound.

c £16.35 is nearer to £20 than it is to £10; so £16.35 = £20 to the nearest ten pounds.

Exercise 2.11

Express each of the following

a to the nearest ten pence
b to the nearest pound
c to the nearest ten pounds.

1 £17.87   **2** £36.94   **3** £57.12
4 £42.43   **5** £63.28   **6** £24.76
7 £38.19   **8** £14.53   **9** £52.98
10 £49.76   **11** £26.07   **12** £30.81

Decimal fractions can be 'rounded off' in a similar way:

4.62 = 4.6 *to the nearest tenth.*

This is usually written

4.62 = 4.6   correct to 1 decimal place
     or   correct to 1 dp

Example 10

a Give 3.74 correct to 1 decimal place.
b Give 4.25 correct to 1 decimal place.
c Give 1.98 correct to 1 decimal place.
d Give 0.486 correct to 2 decimal places.

a 3.74 = 3.7 correct to 1 dp
b 4.25 = 4.3 correct to 1 dp
c 1.98 = 2.0 correct to 1 dp. Note that the answer is not 2 but 2.0 because it is required correct to one decimal place.
d 0.486 = 0.49 correct to 2 dp

Example 11

Find the value of the following, correct to two decimal places.

a $12.7 \div 3.4$ **b** $321 \div 28$

c The cost of 6.78 metres of cloth at £12.34 a metre.

Using an eight-digit display calculator:

a $12.7 \div 3.4 = 3.735\,294\,1$
$= 3.74$ (to 2 dp)

b $321 \div 28 = 11.464\,285$
$= 11.46$ (to 2 dp)

c $6.78 \times £12.34 = £83.6652$
$= £83.67$ (to 2 dp)

Exercise 2.12

For questions **1** to **12**, express each term correct to one decimal place.

1 1.37	**2** 4.59	**3** 5.63	**4** 3.41
5 6.28	**6** 8.76	**7** 7.85	**8** 8.07
9 0.92	**10** 5.14	**11** 2.03	**12** 4.98

For questions **13** to **28**, express each term correct to two decimal places.

13 1.543	**14** 3.954	**15** 2.617	**16** 6.579
17 4.285	**18** 0.892	**19** 5.971	**20** 1.658
21 6.116	**22** 4.509	**23** 3.402	**24** 2.008
25 1.397	**26** 5.698	**27** 4.996	**28** 1.999

For questions **29** to **38**, express each term correct to one decimal place.

29 1.325	**30** 2.536	**31** 5.379	**32** 4.684
33 3.857	**34** 2.073	**35** 0.942	**36** 1.418
37 5.024	**38** 4.963		

For questions **39** to **58**, express each term
a correct to 2 dp   **b** correct to 1 dp

39 4.368	**40** 2.537	**41** 1.724	**42** 0.582
43 5.253	**44** 6.865	**45** 1.397	**46** 4.984
47 2.998	**48** 3.024	**49** 4.039	**50** 5.073
51 1.086	**52** 2.408	**53** 3.204	**54** 4.007
55 5.002	**56** 6.097	**57** 1.055	**58** 0.555

Exercise 2.13

For questions **1-20** find the value correct to one decimal place.

1 $12.3 \div 7$	**2** 67×1.045
3 $0.56 \div 0.25$	**4** 9.76×9.76
5 $327 \div 11$	**6** 0.071×95
7 $524 \div 0.89$	**8** 34.7×14.8
9 $0.7 \div 0.03$	**10** $0.9 \times 0.9 \times 0.9$
11 $5.33 \div 0.9$	**12** 5.33×0.9
13 $67.4 \div 0.72$	**14** 67.4×0.72
15 $1.102 \div 7$	**16** 1.102×7
17 $58.91 \div 2.7$	**18** 58.91×2.7
19 $6.0222 \div 8$	**20** 6.0222×8

For questions **21–40** find the value correct to two decimal places

21 $329 \div 465$	**22** 12.71×71.12
23 $0.65 \div 0.89$	**24** 3.142×8.6
25 $12.47 \div 7$	**26** $0.85 \times 0.85 \times 0.85$
27 $517 \div 35$	**28** 12.47×7.8
29 $623 \div 0.815$	**30** $623 \times 0.9 \times 0.815$
31 $4589 \div 12$	**32** 0.0034×65
33 $0.983 \div 0.451$	**34** 0.983×0.451
35 $0.0045 \div 0.5$	**36** 0.0045×0.5
37 $10.45 \div 1.47$	**38** 10.45×1.47
39 $3.142 \div 17$	**40** 3.142×17

Example 12

A type of cloth costs £3.45 a metre.

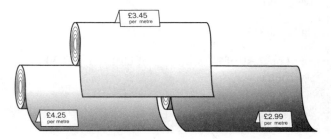

Find the cost of:

a 9 metres   **b** 7.9 metres

a 9 × £3.45 = £31.05

b 7.9 × £3.45 = £27.255
But £27.255 is not a real amount of money, so we must approximate the answer to £27.26.

Exercise 2.14

1 Look at the prices of these cheeses.

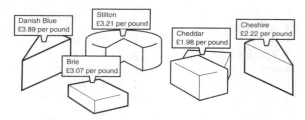

Find the cost of the following.

a 2.7 pounds of Stilton.
b 0.9 pounds of Cheddar.
c 1.2 pounds of Cheshire.
d 1.3 pounds of Brie.
e 0.6 pounds of Danish Blue.
f 0.5 pounds of Stilton and 0.7 pounds of Danish Blue.
g 1.1 pounds of Cheddar and 1.3 pounds of Cheshire.
h 1.5 pounds of Brie and 1.4 pounds each of Stilton and Cheddar.
i 0.2 pounds of Danish Blue, 0.3 pounds of Cheddar and 0.4 pounds of Brie.
j 0.5 pounds of each cheese.

2 A bus company calculates the cost of its fares by charging 12 pence for each mile of the journey. For a return ticket the cost is calculated by adding the two single fares together and then multiplying by 0.9.

Find the cost for these journeys of the following length.

a 8 miles   **b** 8.9 miles   **c** 5.6 miles
d 15.9 miles   **e** 23.2 miles
f a return ticket for a 6.7 mile journey.
g a return ticket for an 8.5 mile journey.
h a return ticket for a 9.3 mile journey.
i a return ticket for a 15.4 mile journey.
j a return ticket for a 22.9 mile journey.

3 Many people form syndicates for the football pools or the National Lottery.

In each case, find the value of each share of the following wins.

a £345 000 shared by 7 people.
b £800 000 shared by 11 people.
c £1 234 555 shared by 3 people.
d £2 768 345 shared by 8 people.
e £517 shared by 35 people.
f £32 777 shared by 16 people.
g £17 234 000 shared by 17 people.
h £10 225 691.53 shared by 2 people.
i £12 671 shared by 9 people.
j £8 234 177 shared by 133 people.

4 This is part of the menu in a pizza restaurant.

Pizzas	Large	Medium	Small
Cheese	£4.56	£3.21	£2.85
Mushroom	£4.86	£3.51	£3.15
Chilli	£4.96	£3.61	£3.25
Drinks			
Beer	£1.42		
Wine	£1.13 (per glass)		
Soft drink	£0.96		

If five friends agree to share the bill equally, how much does each pay if they order

a Two large cheese pizzas, one small chilli pizza, two beers and three glasses of wine.
b One medium mushroom pizza, three medium chilli pizzas and five soft drinks.
c Four large cheese pizzas, three beers and three soft drinks.

d Two large mushroom pizzas, two large chilli pizzas, a small cheese pizza, five glasses of wine and a soft drink.

e Five small chilli pizzas and five beers.

f Four large mushroom pizzas and ten soft drinks.

g A large cheese pizza, a medium mushroom pizza, three small chilli pizzas, three glasses of wine and four soft drinks.

h Two small cheese pizzas, two small mushroom pizzas, one large chilli pizza, four beers, five glasses of wine and three soft drinks.

i Three large chilli pizzas, five beers, five glasses of wine and five soft drinks.

Speed, distance, time

A car travels on a motorway at a constant speed. The journey of 270 km is completed in 3 hours.

So, in 1 hour the car travels a distance of $\frac{270}{3} = 90$ km

We say that the *average speed* of the car is 90 kilometres per hour ($90 \, \text{km} \, \text{h}^{-1}$).

$$\text{average speed } (\text{km} \, \text{h}^{-1}) = \frac{\text{distance travelled (km)}}{\text{time taken (h)}}$$

Example 13

Write as a decimal of one hour

a 15 minutes   **b** 50 minutes   **c** 35 minutes

a $15 \, \text{min} = \frac{15}{60} \, \text{h} = 0.25 \, \text{h}$

b $50 \, \text{min} = \frac{50}{60} \, \text{h} \approx 0.83 \, \text{h}$

c $35 \, \text{min} = \frac{35}{60} \, \text{h} \approx 0.58 \, \text{h}$

Exercise 2.15

Write each of the following as a decimal of one hour.

1	20 minutes	**2**	40 minutes	**3**	30 minutes
4	10 minutes	**5**	12 minutes	**6**	48 minutes
7	24 minutes	**8**	36 minutes	**9**	6 minutes
10	18 minutes	**11**	54 minutes	**12**	5 minutes
13	25 minutes	**14**	55 minutes	**15**	45 minutes
16	4 minutes	**17**	8 minutes	**18**	3 minutes
19	9 minutes	**20**	27 minutes		

Example 14

Find the average speed (in $\text{km} \, \text{h}^{-1}$) for a journey of

a 135 km in 3 hours   **b** 150 km in $2\frac{1}{2}$ hours

a $\text{average speed} = \frac{\text{distance}}{\text{time}} = \frac{135}{3} = 45 \, \text{km} \, \text{h}^{-1}$

b $\text{average speed} = \frac{\text{distance}}{\text{time}} = \frac{150}{2\frac{1}{2}} = 150 \div 2.5$

$= 60 \, \text{km} \, \text{h}^{-1}$

Exercise 2.16

Find the average speed for each of the following journeys.

	distance covered	*time taken*		*distance covered*	*time taken*
1	100 cm	2 h	**2**	180 km	3 h
3	220 km	4 h	**4**	420 km	5 h
5	378 km	6 h	**6**	656 km	8 h
7	536 km	4 h	**8**	708 km	6 h
9	515 km	5 h	**10**	630 km	6 h
11	100 km	$2\frac{1}{2}$ h	**12**	120 km	$1\frac{1}{2}$ h
13	270 km	$4\frac{1}{2}$ h	**14**	350 km	$3\frac{1}{2}$ h
15	125 km	$2\frac{1}{2}$ h	**16**	108 km	$1\frac{1}{2}$ h
17	150 km	$1\frac{1}{4}$ h	**18**	140 km	$1\frac{3}{4}$ h
19	90 km	$2\frac{1}{4}$ h	**20**	330 km	$2\frac{3}{4}$ h

Example 15

Find the average speed (in $\text{km} \, \text{h}^{-1}$) for a journey of

a 30 km in 20 min   **b** 165 km in 2 h 45 min

a $\text{average speed} = \frac{\text{distance (km)}}{\text{time (h)}}$

$= 30 \div (20 \div 60)$

Using a calculator

$20 \div 60 = 0.333\,333\,3$

$30 \div (20 \div 60) = 90 \, \text{km} \, \text{h}^{-1}$

b $\text{average speed} = \frac{\text{distance (km)}}{\text{time (h)}} = \frac{165}{2\frac{45}{60}} = \frac{165}{2.75}$

$= 165 \div 2.75$

$= 60 \, \text{km} \, \text{h}^{-1}$

Exercise 2.17

For questions **1** to **14**, find the average speed for each journey.

	distance covered	time taken		distance covered	time taken
1	150 km	1 h 30 min	**2**	120 km	2 h 30 min
3	90 km	1 h 15 min	**4**	105 km	1 h 45 min
5	189 km	2 h 15 min	**6**	275 km	2 h 45 min
7	100 km	1 h 20 min	**8**	160 km	1 h 40 min
9	126 km	2 h 20 min	**10**	18 km	15 min
11	36 km	45 min	**12**	35 km	30 min
13	45 km	20 min	**14**	72 km	40 min

15 A train travels a distance of 161 km from London to Leicester in 1 h 45 min.
Find the average speed.

16 A train travels a distance of 630 km from London to Edinburgh in 4 h 30 min.
Find the average speed.

17 A man drives his car a distance of 135 km from London to Dover in 2 h 15 min.
Find his average speed.

18 A bus travels a distance of 98 km from Newcastle to Berwick in 2 h 20 min.
Find the average speed.

19 A woman drives her car a distance of 13 km from Birmingham to Halesowen in 20 min.
Find her average speed.

20 A bus travels a distance of 24 km from Leeds to Harrogate in 45 min.
Find the average speed.

If a car travels at an average speed of 60 km h^{-1}

then, in 1 hour it travels $60 \times 1 = 60 \text{ km}$
in 2 hours it travels $60 \times 2 = 120 \text{ km} \ldots$
and so on.

Example 16

Find the distance travelled when a car travels for

a 4 hours at an average speed of 45 km h^{-1}

b $2\frac{1}{2}$ hours at an average speed of 60 km h^{-1}

c 20 minutes at an average speed of 75 km h^{-1}

a distance $= 45 \times 4 = 180 \text{ km}$

b distance $= 60 \times 2.5 = 150 \text{ km}$

c distance $= 75 \times \dfrac{20}{60} = \dfrac{75 \times 20}{60} = 25 \text{ km}$

Exercise 2.18

For questions **1** to **30**, find the distance covered for each journey.

	average speed	time of journey		average speed	time of journey
1	80 km h^{-1}	3 hours	**2**	90 km h^{-1}	4 hours
3	75 km h^{-1}	6 hours	**4**	45 km h^{-1}	8 hours
5	34 km h^{-1}	5 hours	**6**	55 km h^{-1}	7 hours
7	125 km h^{-1}	4 hours	**8**	141 km h^{-1}	3 hours
9	108 km h^{-1}	5 hours	**10**	50 km h^{-1}	$1\frac{1}{2}$ hours
11	80 km h^{-1}	$2\frac{1}{2}$ hours	**12**	40 km h^{-1}	$4\frac{1}{2}$ hours
13	160 km h^{-1}	$1\frac{1}{4}$ hours	**14**	40 km h^{-1}	$1\frac{3}{4}$ hours
15	80 km h^{-1}	$2\frac{1}{4}$ hours	**16**	160 km h^{-1}	$2\frac{3}{4}$ hours
17	64 km h^{-1}	$\frac{1}{4}$ hour	**18**	120 km h^{-1}	$\frac{3}{4}$ hour
19	70 km h^{-1}	1 h 30 min	**20**	36 km h^{-1}	2 h 30 min
21	84 km h^{-1}	1 h 15 min	**22**	120 km h^{-1}	1 h 45 min
23	72 km h^{-1}	2 h 15 min	**24**	90 km h^{-1}	1 h 20 min
25	48 km h^{-1}	1 h 40 min	**26**	63 km h^{-1}	2 h 20 min
27	96 km h^{-1}	15 min	**28**	84 km h^{-1}	45 min
29	48 km h^{-1}	20 min	**30**	90 km h^{-1}	40 min

31 A car travelling at an average speed of 75 km h^{-1} takes 4 hours to travel from London to Manchester.
Find the distance between the two cities.

32 A train travelling at an average speed of 125 km h^{-1} takes 3 hours to travel from London (King's Cross) to Darlington.
Find the distance between the two stations.

33 A train travelling at an average speed of 94 km h^{-1} takes 9 hours to travel from London (King's Cross) to Aberdeen.
Find the distance between the two stations.

34 A train travelling at an average speed of 128 km h^{-1} takes 1 h 30 min to travel from London (Paddington) to Bristol.
Find the distance between the two stations.

35 A car travelling at an average speed of 66 km h^{-1} takes 3 h 30 min to travel from Newcastle to Glasgow.
Find the distance between the two cities.

36 A car travelling at an average speed of 64 km h^{-1} takes 1 h 15 min to travel from Leeds to Hull.
Find the distance between the two cities.

37 A bus travelling at an average speed of 28 km h^{-1} takes 2 h 15 min to travel from Birmingham to Shrewsbury.
Find the distance between the two bus stations.

38 A ship sailing at an average speed of $27\,\mathrm{km\,h}^{-1}$ takes 1 h 20 min to cross the English Channel from Dover to Calais.
Find the distance between the two ports.

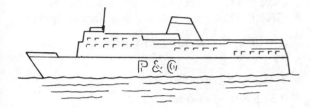

39 A car travelling at an average speed of $54\,\mathrm{km\,h}^{-1}$ takes 20 minutes to travel from Brighton to Worthing.
Find the distance between the two resorts.

40 An aeroplane travelling at $480\,\mathrm{km\,h}^{-1}$ takes 45 minutes to fly from Birmingham to Dublin.
Find the distance between the two airports.

If an aeroplane flies at an average speed of $500\,\mathrm{km\,h}^{-1}$, then
it would take 1 hour to fly a distance of 500 km
it would take 2 hours to fly a distance of 1000 km
(i.e. $1000 \div 500$)
it would take 3 hours to fly a distance of 1500 km
(i.e. $1500 \div 500$)
... and so on

Example 17

Find the time taken to travel a distance of

a 750 km at an average speed of $75\,\mathrm{km\,h}^{-1}$
b 150 km at an average speed of $60\,\mathrm{km\,h}^{-1}$
c 60 km at an average speed of $80\,\mathrm{km\,h}^{-1}$

a Time taken $= 750 \div 75 = \dfrac{750}{75}\,\mathrm{h} = 10\,\mathrm{h}$

b Time taken $= 150 \div 60 = \dfrac{150}{60}\,\mathrm{h} = 2.5\,\mathrm{h}$

c Time taken $= 60 \div 80 = \dfrac{60}{80}\,\mathrm{h} = 0.75\,\mathrm{h}$
$= 45\,\mathrm{min}$

Exercise 2.19

For questions **1** to **30**, find the time taken for each journey.

	distance covered	average speed		distance covered	average speed
1	150 km	$50\,\mathrm{km\,h}^{-1}$	**2**	320 km	$80\,\mathrm{km\,h}^{-1}$
3	240 km	$30\,\mathrm{km\,h}^{-1}$	**4**	200 km	$40\,\mathrm{km\,h}^{-1}$
5	360 km	$60\,\mathrm{km\,h}^{-1}$	**6**	175 km	$25\,\mathrm{km\,h}^{-1}$
7	140 km	$35\,\mathrm{km\,h}^{-1}$	**8**	600 km	$75\,\mathrm{km\,h}^{-1}$
9	180 km	$36\,\mathrm{km\,h}^{-1}$	**10**	126 km	$42\,\mathrm{km\,h}^{-1}$
11	288 km	$48\,\mathrm{km\,h}^{-1}$	**12**	224 km	$56\,\mathrm{km\,h}^{-1}$
13	441 km	$63\,\mathrm{km\,h}^{-1}$	**14**	486 km	$54\,\mathrm{km\,h}^{-1}$
15	90 km	$60\,\mathrm{km\,h}^{-1}$	**16**	175 km	$70\,\mathrm{km\,h}^{-1}$
17	210 km	$60\,\mathrm{km\,h}^{-1}$	**18**	225 km	$50\,\mathrm{km\,h}^{-1}$
19	60 km	$48\,\mathrm{km\,h}^{-1}$	**20**	63 km	$36\,\mathrm{km\,h}^{-1}$
21	144 km	$64\,\mathrm{km\,h}^{-1}$	**22**	220 km	$80\,\mathrm{km\,h}^{-1}$
23	56 km	$42\,\mathrm{km\,h}^{-1}$	**24**	80 km	$48\,\mathrm{km\,h}^{-1}$
25	126 km	$54\,\mathrm{km\,h}^{-1}$	**26**	192 km	$72\,\mathrm{km\,h}^{-1}$
27	24 km	$96\,\mathrm{km\,h}^{-1}$	**28**	81 km	$108\,\mathrm{km\,h}^{-1}$
29	28 km	$84\,\mathrm{km\,h}^{-1}$	**30**	96 km	$144\,\mathrm{km\,h}^{-1}$

31 Find the time taken by a train which travels a distance of 480 km from London to Penzance at an average speed of $96\,\mathrm{km\,h}^{-1}$.

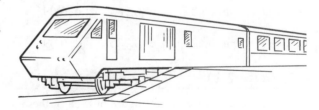

32 Find the time taken by a car which travels a distance of 432 km from London to Newcastle at an average speed of $72\,\mathrm{km\,h}^{-1}$.

33 Find the time taken by a car which travels a distance of 630 km from Bristol to Glasgow at an average speed of $70\,\mathrm{km\,h}^{-1}$.

34 Find the time taken by a train which travels a distance of 405 km from London to Holyhead at an average speed of $90\,\mathrm{km\,h}^{-1}$.

35 Find the time taken by a train which travels a distance of 275 km from London to Exeter at an average speed of $110\,\mathrm{km\,h}^{-1}$.

36 Find the time taken by a bus which travels a distance of 56 km from Liverpool to Manchester at an average speed of $32\,\mathrm{km\,h}^{-1}$.

37 Find the time taken by a car which travels a distance of 140 km from Birmingham to Bristol at an average speed of $84\,\mathrm{km\,h}^{-1}$.

16

38 Find the time taken by a train which travels a distance of 297 km from London to Leeds at an average speed of 132 km h^{-1}.

39 Find the time taken by an aeroplane which flies a distance of 125 km from Manchester to Birmingham at 500 km h^{-1}.

40 Find the time taken by an aeroplane which flies a distance of 320 km from Leeds to Belfast at 480 km h^{-1}.

Significant figures

The first non-zero digit of the number is called the *first significant figure* of the number.

Example 18

Underline the first significant figure of each of these numbers.

a 2793   **b** 65.27   **c** 0.785   **d** 0.09

a 2<u>7</u>93   **b** <u>6</u>5.27   **c** 0.<u>7</u>85   **d** 0.0<u>9</u>

Exercise 2.20

Underline the first significant figure of each of these numbers.

1 34	**2** 506	**3** 6.7
4 0.55	**5** 6.09	**6** 0.05
7 0.001 09	**8** 1000.6	**9** 1999
10 0.004	**11** 0.010 101	**12** 0.000 010 999
13 120 000	**14** 0.0012	**15** 10 000
16 0.001 07		

Numbers can be approximated and rounded to a number of *significant figures* as well as to a number of decimal places.

When rounding to a number of significant figures you always start with the first significant figure.

You then count out the number of significant figures you require and apply normal rules for rounding.

Example 19

a Give 37.5 correct to 2 significant figures.
b Give 3.75 correct to 2 significant figures.
c Give 0.342 correct to 2 significant figures.
d Give 0.003 42 correct to 2 significant figures.

We write sf for 'significant figures'.

a 37.5 = 38 correct to 2 sf

b 3.75 = 3.8 correct to 2 sf

c 0.342 = 0.34 correct to 2 sf

d 0.003 42 = 0.0034 correct to 2 sf

Exercise 2.21

Give each number correct to 2 significant figures.

1 67.8	**2** 78.3	**3** 56.1
4 75.7	**5** 39.9	**6** 23.8
7 92.7	**8** 12.5	**9** 21.1
10 67.6	**11** 3.05	**12** 7.89
13 4.51	**14** 4.15	**15** 5.14
16 5.41	**17** 1.45	**18** 1.54
19 5.99	**20** 0.567	**21** 0.826
22 0.862	**23** 0.682	**24** 0.628
25 0.0457	**26** 0.0317	**27** 0.0371
28 0.0713	**29** 0.0731	**30** 34.9
31 34.2	**32** 77.7	**33** 6.709
34 0.004 27	**35** 17.855	

Example 20

a Give 425.7 correct to 3 significant figures.
b Give 3.75 correct to 1 significant figure.
c Give 0.3429 correct to 3 significant figures.
d Give 0.003 42 correct to 1 significant figure.

a 425.7 = 426 correct to 3 sf

b 3.75 = 4 correct to 1 sf

c 0.3429 = 0.343 correct to 3 sf

d 0.003 42 = 0.003 correct to 1 sf

Exercise 2.22

In questions **1** to **15**, give each number correct to three significant figures.

1 375.3	**2** 373.5	**3** 733.5
4 735.3	**5** 537.3	**6** 7.893
7 6.625	**8** 6.261	**9** 6.126
10 9.015	**11** 0.036 21	**12** 0.045 83
13 0.005 555 5	**14** 0.002 199	**15** 0.000 151 5

In questions **16** to **30**, give each number correct to one significant figure.

16 5.56	**17** 8.09	**18** 7.73
19 7.37	**20** 6.72	**21** 6.27
22 2.67	**23** 2.76	**24** 2.51
25 2.99	**26** 0.051	**27** 0.054
28 0.0059	**29** 0.0055	**30** 0.0365

Example 21

a Give 347.9 correct to 1 significant figure.
b Give 375.4 correct to 2 significant figures.
c Give 375 200 correct to 3 significant figures.

a 347.9 = 300 correct to 1 sf. Note that the answer is 300, not 3, which would be a very poor approximation for 347.9

b 375.4 = 380 correct to 2 sf

c 375 200 = 375 000 correct to 3 sf

Exercise 2.23

1 Give each number correct to 3 sf.

a 2345	**b** 2354	**c** 2453
d 2435	**e** 2543	**f** 2534
g 3245	**h** 3254	**i** 3452
j 3425	**k** 1256	**l** 9999
m 345.9	**n** 3459.3	**o** 9009.7
p 10 583	**q** 87 450	**r** 87 853
s 88 888	**t** 44 444	**u** 33 333
v 151 515	**w** 223 344	**x** 667 788

2 Give each number in question **1** correct to 2 sf.

3 Give each number in question **1** correct to 1 sf.

Estimating

Example 22

Estimate the value of $(3.4 \times 27.8) \div 7.3$

Rounding each number to 1 significant figure gives the estimate

$$(3 \times 30) \div 7 = 90 \div 7$$
$$= 10 \text{ to } 1 \text{ sf}$$

The calculated answer is 13.0 correct to 1 dp.

Exercise 2.24

In questions **1** to **30**, estimate the value of each calculation, giving your estimate correct to 1 significant figure.
Use a calculator to find an answer correct to 1 dp and write this after your estimate.

1 3.45×7.27	**2** $45.6 \div 4.73$
3 89.7×1.237	**4** $89.7 \div 1.237$
5 92.6×3.69	**6** $67.8 \div 4.81$
7 653×2.99	**8** $653 \div 2.99$
9 0.685×111	**10** $187 \div 1.92$
11 613×9.73	**12** $79.5 \div 2.99$
13 759×76.2	**14** $861 \div 86.7$
15 345×30.1	**16** $29.9 \div 2.01$
17 2345×2.45	**18** $65.4 \div 11.83$
19 73.9×4.01	**20** $42.43 \div 7.63$
21 $(23.6 \times 2.89) \div 5.1$	**22** $(89.2 \times 21) \div 17.6$
23 $(98.1 \times 4.09) \div 7.62$	**24** $(675 \times 2.49) \div 142.9$
25 $(201 \times 3.55) \div 378$	**26** $(8.93 \times 27.4) \div 8.73$
27 $(75.2 \times 99.9) \div 6753$	**28** $(90.3 \times 87.3) \div 7703$
29 $(23.4 \times 78.9) \div 32.3$	**30** $(62.8 \times 25.3) \div 97.1$

31 There are 650 children in a school who each spend £6.25 a week on school meals.
  a Estimate correct to 1 sf the total amount spent each week on school meals.
  b Calculate correct to 1 dp the total amount spent each week on school meals.

32 A carpet costs £7.89 a square metre.

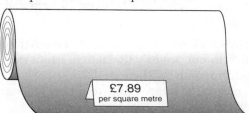

£7.89 per square metre

  a Estimate correct to 1 sf the area of a piece of carpet 2.5 metres by 4.3 metres.
  b Estimate correct to 1 sf the price of a piece of carpet 2.5 metres by 4.3 metres.
  c Calculate correct to 1 dp the price of a piece of carpet 2.5 metres by 4.3 metres.

33 A car averages 14.7 kilometres per litre of petrol. It uses petrol which costs 54.9 p per litre.
  a Estimate correct to 1 sf the quantity of petrol used during a journey of 293.8 km.
  b Estimate correct to the nearest 10 p the cost of the petrol used during a journey of 293.8 km.
  c Calculate correct to 1 dp the cost of the petrol used during a journey of 293.8 km.

34 A train travels 214.8 miles in 3 hours 45 minutes.
  a Estimate correct to 1 sf the average speed for the journey.
  b Calculate correct to 1 dp the average speed for the journey.

35 A syndicate of 12 people plays ten lines each week on the National Lottery. One week they win 3 prizes of £187 and 4 prizes of £10.

  a Estimate correct to 1 sf each person's share of the prize money.
  b Calculate correct to 2 dp each person's share of the prize money.

A length measured correct to a given unit will have a real length that lies between two limits.

For example, if a length is measured as 20 cm, correct to the nearest centimetre, the actual length can be anywhere between 19.5 cm and 20.5 cm.

Strictly speaking the length could be anything up to 20.5 cm but not exactly 20.5 cm, since this would round up to 21 cm.
This means the upper limit would be 20.49 cm or 20.499 cm or 20.4999 cm and so on.

For practical reasons the upper limit is therefore taken as 20.5 cm, even though this is technically incorrect.

Example 23

Between what limits will a length measured as 25 m correct to the nearest metre lie?

The length will be between 24.5 m and 25.5 m.

Exercise 2.25

State the limits that each measurement must lie between.

1 A weight of 2 kg correct to the nearest kilogram.
2 A length of 100 m correct to the nearest metre.
3 A length of 100 cm correct to the nearest centimetre.
4 A time of 65 minutes correct to the nearest minute.
5 An area of 60 cm² correct to the nearest square centimetre.
6 A length of 56 mm correct to the nearest millimetre.
7 A weight of 55 g correct to the nearest gram.
8 A weight of 500 g correct to the nearest gram.
9 A time of 3 minutes correct to the nearest minute.
10 An area of 25 m² correct to the nearest square metre.

Example 24

A square carpet tile is manufactured so that its side length is 30 cm, correct to the nearest centimetre.

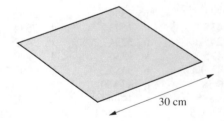

30 cm

  a Within what limits will the side length of a carpet tile lie?
  b What is the least area a carpet tile can have?
  c What is the greatest area a carpet tile can have?

  a The side length of the carpet tile will be between 29.5 cm and 30.5 cm.

  b The least area a carpet tile can have is $29.5 \times 29.5 = 870.25 \, \text{cm}^2$

  c The greatest area a carpet tile can have is $30.5 \times 30.5 = 930.25 \, \text{cm}^2$

Exercise 2.26

1 A trap door 50 cm wide by 90 cm long (correct to the nearest cm) is cut from a sheet of plywood.

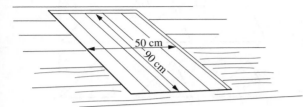

a What is the least possible width for the trapdoor?
b What is the greatest possible width for the trapdoor?
c What is the least possible length for the trapdoor?
d What is the greatest possible length for the trapdoor?
e What is the least possible area for the trapdoor?
f What is the greatest possible area for the trapdoor?

2 A car completes a 240 mile journey (correct to the nearest mile) at an average speed of 60 miles per hour, correct to the nearest mile per hour.
a What is the least possible value for the average speed of the car?
b What is the greatest possible value for the average speed of the car?
c What is the least possible value for the length of the journey?
d What is the greatest possible value for the length of the journey?
e What is the least possible time the journey will take?
f What is the greatest possible time the journey will take?

3 A length of cloth is 25 metres long (to the nearest metre). It is to be cut into pieces of length 80 cm (to the nearest centimetre).
a What is the least possible value for the length of the cloth in metres?
b What is the greatest possible value for the length of the cloth in metres?
c What is the least possible value for the length of the cloth in centimetres?
d What is the greatest possible value for the length of the cloth in centimetres?
e What is the least possible value for the length of each piece in centimetres?

f What is the greatest possible value for the length of each piece in centimetres?
g What is the least number of pieces which can be cut from the cloth?
h What is the greatest number of pieces which can be cut from the cloth?

4 A window has 8 separate panes of glass, each 200 mm wide by 300 mm high (to the nearest millimetre).

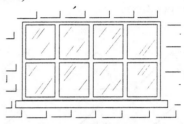

a What is the least possible width for one pane of glass?
b What is the greatest possible width for one pane of glass?
c What is the least possible area of glass in the window?
d What is the greatest possible area of glass in the window?

5 A square garden has side 55 m long (correct to the nearest metre). It is to be covered with grass seed which comes in boxes that cover 64 m² (correct to the nearest square metre).

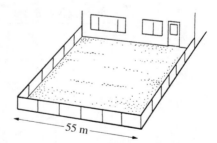

a What is the least possible value for the side length of the garden?
b What is the greatest possible value for the side length of the garden?
c What is the least possible value for the area of the garden?
d What is the greatest possible value for the area of the garden?
e What is the least number of boxes of seed that will be required?
f What is the greatest number of boxes of seed that will be required?

Unit 3 Transformations

Translations

We have already looked at two different types of *transformation*: reflection and rotation.

Translation is another kind of transformation.

Example 1

This diagram shows a shaded triangle moved to eight new positions

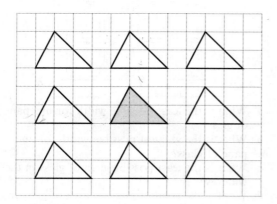

Describe the translation that moves the shaded triangle to each new position.

Translations are defined by two numbers in a bracket.

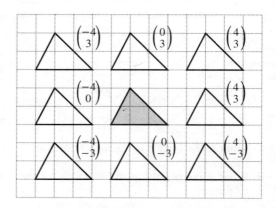

These are the horizontal and vertical distances moved by each point on the shape.

$$\left(\begin{array}{c} \xleftarrow{-} \text{ horizontal movement } \xrightarrow{+} \\ \uparrow+ \\ \text{vertical movement} \\ \downarrow- \end{array} \right)$$

Exercise 3.1

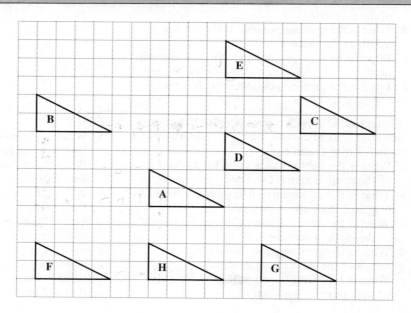

Describe the translation which moves the first triangle on to the second triangle.

1 A to B	**2** A to C	**3** A to D
4 A to E	**5** A to F	**6** A to G
7 A to H	**8** B to A	**9** B to C
10 B to D	**11** B to E	**12** B to F
13 B to G	**14** B to H	**15** C to A
16 C to B	**17** C to D	**18** C to E
19 C to F	**20** C to G	**21** C to H
22 D to A	**23** D to B	**24** D to C
25 D to E	**26** D to F	**27** D to G
28 D to H	**29** E to A	**30** E to B
31 E to C	**32** E to D	**33** E to F
34 E to G	**35** E to H	**36** F to A
37 F to B	**38** F to C	**39** F to D
40 F to E	**41** F to G	**42** F to H

Example 2

The triangle P has vertices (corner points) at (2, 7), (3, 4) and 6, 5).
Show on one graph the triangle P and its images Q, R and S after the translations

$$\begin{pmatrix} 3 \\ -4 \end{pmatrix} \quad \begin{pmatrix} 2 \\ 3 \end{pmatrix} \quad \begin{pmatrix} -2 \\ -3 \end{pmatrix}$$

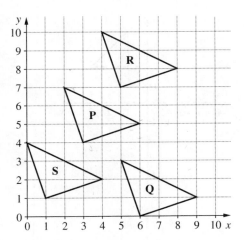

Exercise 3.2

1 The triangle P has vertices at (2, 7), (3, 4) and (6, 5).
Show on one graph the triangle P and its images Q, R and S after the translations

$$\begin{pmatrix} 3 \\ 3 \end{pmatrix} \quad \begin{pmatrix} 0 \\ -4 \end{pmatrix} \quad \begin{pmatrix} -2 \\ 3 \end{pmatrix}$$

2 The triangle W has vertices at (0, 0), (0, 2) and (4, 2).
Show on one graph the triangle W and its images X, Y and Z after the translations

$$\begin{pmatrix} 6 \\ 6 \end{pmatrix} \quad \begin{pmatrix} 0 \\ 6 \end{pmatrix} \quad \begin{pmatrix} 6 \\ 0 \end{pmatrix}$$

3 The triangle A has vertices at (7, 8), (10, 8) and (9, 10).
Show on one graph the triangle A and its images B, C and D after the translations

$$\begin{pmatrix} -6 \\ -6 \end{pmatrix} \quad \begin{pmatrix} 0 \\ -6 \end{pmatrix} \quad \begin{pmatrix} -6 \\ 0 \end{pmatrix}$$

4 The triangle J has vertices (7, 8), (10, 8) and (9, 10).
Show on one graph the triangle A and its images K, L and M after the translations

$$\begin{pmatrix} 4 \\ 2 \end{pmatrix} \quad \begin{pmatrix} 4 \\ -2 \end{pmatrix} \quad \begin{pmatrix} 0 \\ 4 \end{pmatrix}$$

5 The rectangle E has vertices at (1, 1), (1, 2), (3, 1) and (3, 2).
Show on one graph the rectangle E and its images F, G and H after the translations

$$\begin{pmatrix} -1 \\ -1 \end{pmatrix} \quad \begin{pmatrix} 7 \\ 7 \end{pmatrix} \quad \begin{pmatrix} 7 \\ -1 \end{pmatrix}$$

6 The hexagon S has vertices at (3, 5), (3, 6), (4, 7), (5, 6), (5, 5) and (4, 4).
Show on one graph the hexagon S and its images T, U and V after the translations

$$\begin{pmatrix} 0 \\ -4 \end{pmatrix} \quad \begin{pmatrix} 5 \\ 3 \end{pmatrix} \quad \begin{pmatrix} -3 \\ 1 \end{pmatrix}$$

To remind you

There are three ways of transforming a point (or a shape) from one position to another.

(1) A *translation*. Here the point is moved a set distance in a set direction.

(2) A *reflection*. Here the point is moved to the same distance on the other side of the mirror line.

(3) A *rotation*. Here the point is turned through a set angle about the point of rotation.

Example 3

Describe the transformation that moves the shaded triangle to each of positions A, B and C.

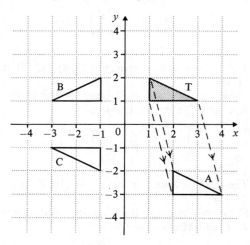

In the diagram

a triangle T is transformed to A by the translation

$$\begin{pmatrix} 1 \\ -4 \end{pmatrix}$$

b triangle T is transformed to B by a reflection in the line $x = 0$, the y-axis.

c triangle T is transformed to C by a rotation of 180° about (0, 0), the origin.

Exercise 3.3

Copy each diagram on to squared paper, then draw the image formed

a by reflection in the x-axis
b by reflection in the y-axis.

1
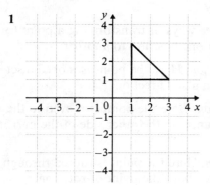

2
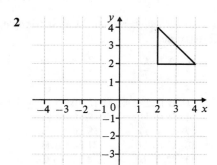

3
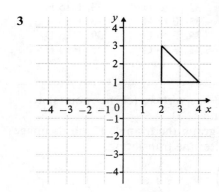

4
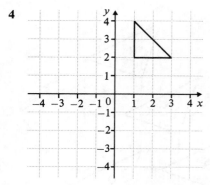

5
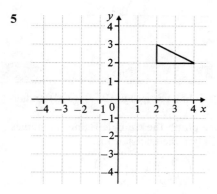

6
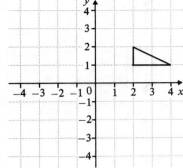

1
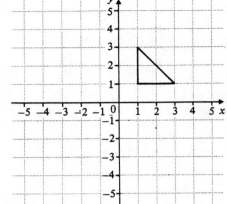

7
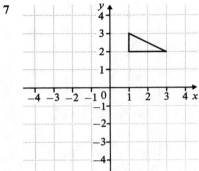

2
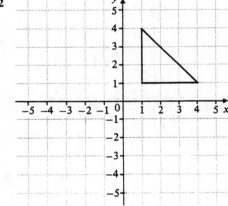

8
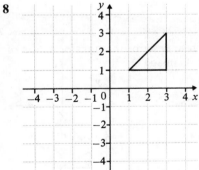

3
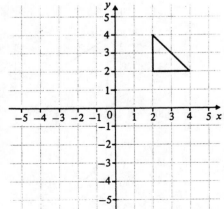

Exercise 3.4

Copy each diagram on to squared paper, then draw
the image formed by rotation about (0, 0)

a through 180°
b through 90° anticlockwise
c through 90° clockwise

24

4

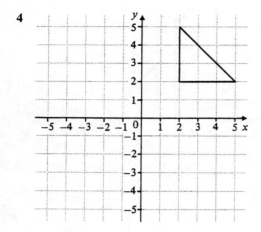

5

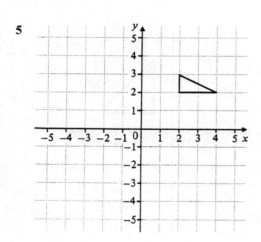

6

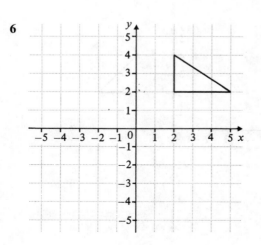

7

8

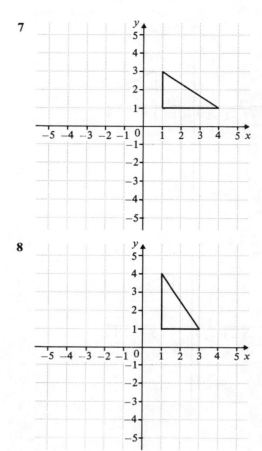

Exercise 3.5

Write a translation to describe the transformation of each triangle P to its image Q.

1

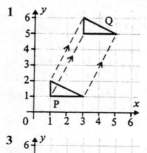

2

3

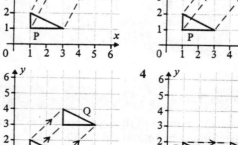

4

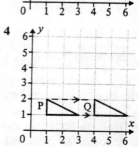

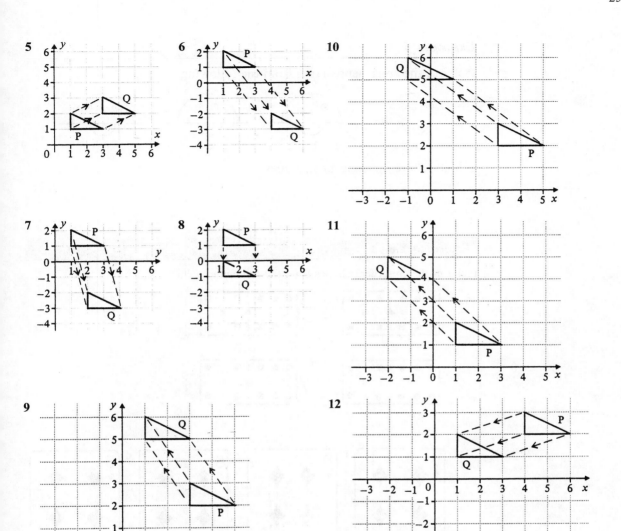

Congruence

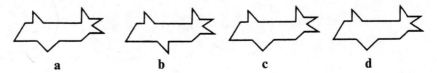

| a | b | c | d |

If you look at the above drawings carefully you should see that three of
them, **a**, **c** and **d** are exactly the same.

Shapes that are alike in every possible way – sides, angles and area – are
said to be *congruent*.

Example 4

Pick out the congruent shapes from the following.

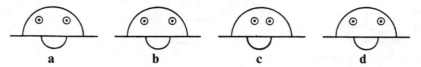

| a | b | c | d |

a, **b** and **d** are the congruent shapes.

Exercise 3.6

Pick out the congruent shapes from the following.

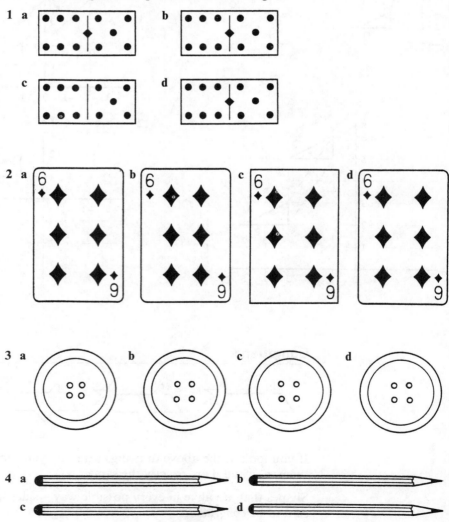

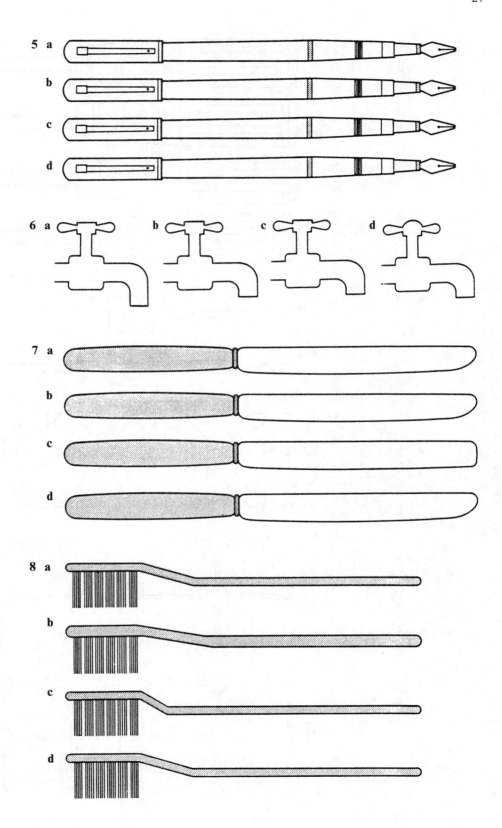

5 a
  b
  c
  d

6 a   b   c   d

7 a
  b
  c
  d

8 a
  b
  c
  d

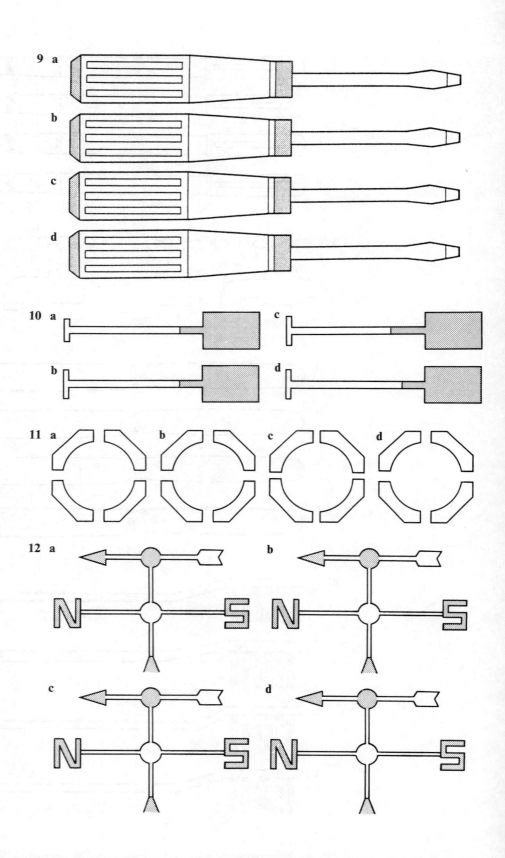

Example 5

Identify the pairs of congruent triangles on this graph.
Describe the transformation which will move one on to the other.

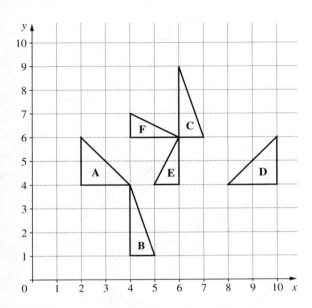

A can be moved on to D with a reflection in the line $x = 6$.

E can be moved on to F with a rotation of $-90°$ about the point (6, 6).

B can be moved on to C with the translation $\begin{pmatrix} 2 \\ 5 \end{pmatrix}$

Exercise 3.7

On each of the following graphs, identify the pairs of congruent triangles.
Describe the transformation which will move one on to the other.

1

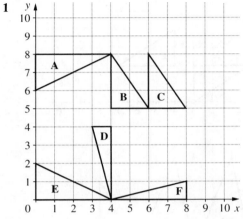

2

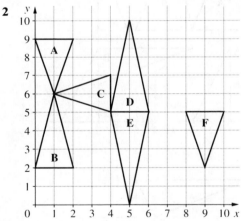

3

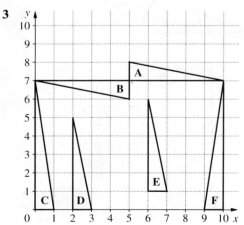

4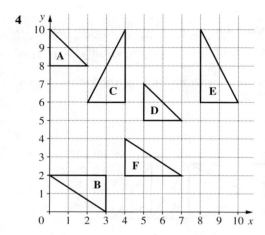

7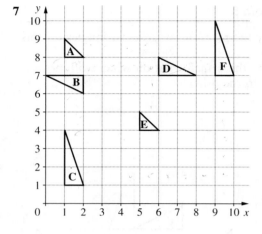

5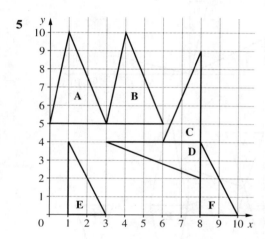

8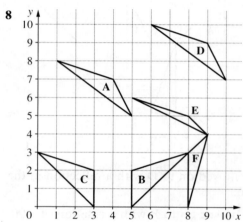

6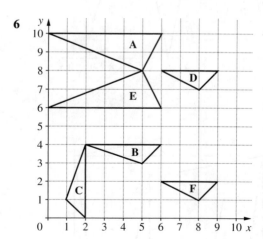

9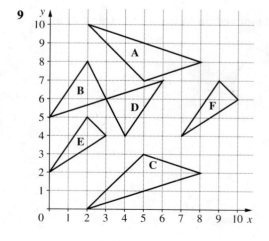

Unit 4   Line graphs

Example 1

The table gives the outside temperature in degrees Celsius at two-hourly intervals on a certain day in November.

time	6 a.m.	8 a.m.	10 a.m.	12 noon	2 p.m.	4 p.m.	6 p.m.	8 p.m.	10 p.m.
temperature °C	0	1	2	9	14	10	5	3	0

Using a scale of 1 cm to 1 hour on the horizontal axis, and 1 cm to 1 degree Celsius on the vertical axis, draw a line graph to illustrate the above information.

From your graph, estimate

a the temperature at 11 a.m. and at 3 p.m.
b the two-hour period during which the temperature rises the most rapidly and by how many degrees.

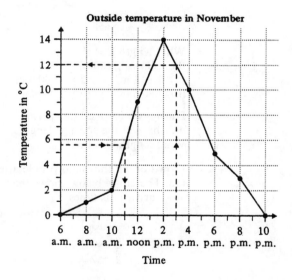

Here are the steps you should take in drawing the graph.

1 Draw two lines at right angles to each other on the graph paper to form the axes, one vertical and one horizontal.
2 Divide these two axes into equal parts, using the scales given.
3 Label the points which mark the equal parts on the axes and give each axis a suitable title, e.g. temperature in °C.
4 Plot the points given in the question, and join up the points.
5 Give the graph a suitable title.

From the graph,

a the temperature is 5.5 °C at 11 a.m. and 12 °C at 3 p.m.
b the temperature rises the most rapidly between 10 a.m. and 12 noon. During this time, the temperature rises by 7 °C.

Exercise 4.1

1 Mrs Jackson spent all day knitting a scarf. She started at 8 a.m. and finished at 5 p.m. The final length of the scarf was one metre. The graph below shows her progress.

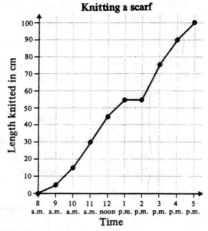

Knitting a scarf

a What length had she knitted by the following times?
  (i) 9.30 a.m.   (ii) 12.30 p.m.
  (ii) 2.30 p.m.   (iv) 4.30 p.m.

b During which one-hour period did she knit the greatest length? What length was this?

c During which one-hour period did she knit the shortest length? What length was this?

d Between what times did Mrs Jackson take a lunch break?

2 A crowd of ten thousand people attended a football match which started at 3 p.m. The graph below shows the number of people who had entered the ground at various times.

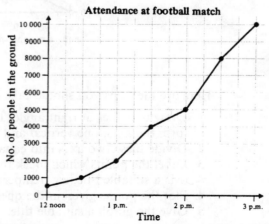

Attendance at football match

a How many people had entered the ground by the following times?
  (i) 1.15 p.m.   (ii) 2.15 p.m.
  (iii) 12.45 p.m.   (iv) 1.45 p.m.
  (v) 2.45 p.m.

b During which half-hour interval did the most people enter the ground? How many people was this?

3 A group of hikers walked 20 km between 10 a.m. and 2.30 p.m. The graph below shows how far they had walked at various times.

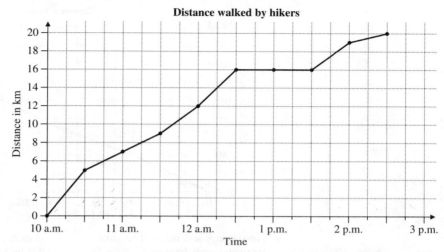

Distance walked by hikers

a What distance had the hikers walked by the following times?
  (i) 11.15 a.m.   (ii) 12.15 p.m.
  (iii) 10.45 a.m.   (iv) 12.45 p.m.

b During which half-hour interval did they walk the furthest? What distance was this?

c Between which times did they stop for lunch?

4 On a long journey by car, I recorded the number of litres of petrol in the tank every 100 km. The graph shows this information.

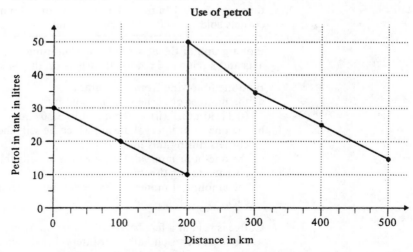

Use of petrol

a How many litres of petrol were in the tank after
  (i) 350 km?   (ii) 450 km?
  (iii) 50 km?   (iv) 150 km?

b Over which 100-km stretch did I use the most petrol? How many litres was this?

c How much petrol did I use over the whole 500-km journey?

5 A boy ran an 800-metre race. The time he took to run a given distance in the race is shown in the graph below.

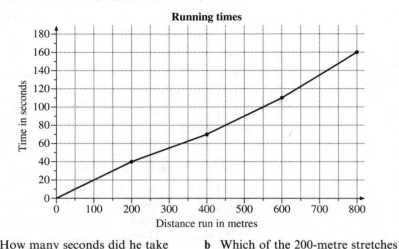

Running times

Time in seconds (y-axis, 0 to 180)

Distance run in metres (x-axis, 0 to 800)

a How many seconds did he take from the start to run
  (i) 100 m?   (ii) 500 m?.
 (iii) 550 m?   (iv) 450 m?
  (v) 150 m?   (vi) 50 m?

b Which of the 200-metre stretches did he run the quickest?
How many seconds did it take him?

c Which of the 200-metre stretches did he run the slowest?
How many seconds did it take him?

6 A man sells ice cream between 10 a.m. and 4 p.m. The table below shows how many cornets he has sold at the end of successive hourly intervals.

time	10 a.m.	11 a.m.	12 noon	1 p.m.	2 p.m.	3 p.m.	4 p.m.
cornets sold	0	20	60	160	240	280	400

Plot a graph of the above information using a scale of 2 cm to 1 hour on the *x*-axis and a scale of 1 cm to 20 cornets on the *y*-axis.

Find the following from your graph.
a the number of cornets he has sold by
  (i) 11.30 a.m. (ii) 2.30 p.m. (iii) 3.30 p.m. (iv) 10.30 a.m. (v) 12.30 p.m.
b the one-hour interval during which he sells the most cornets, and how many cornets during this hour.
c the one-hour interval during which he sells the least cornets, and how many cornets during this hour.
d the amount of money he has taken by 1.30 p.m. if he sells the cornets at 15 p each.

7 Coffee is sold at a fête between 2 p.m. and 6 p.m. The number of litres remaining in the urn after each half-hour interval is shown in the table below.

time	2.00 p.m.	2.30 p.m.	3.00 p.m.	3.30 p.m.	4.00 p.m.	4.00 p.m.
no. of litres	20	18	15	14	10	20

time	4.30 p.m.	5.00 p.m.	5.30 p.m.	6.00 p.m.
no. of litres	15	11	5	2

The urn was refilled at 4.00 p.m.
Plot a graph of this information using a scale of 4 cm to 1 hour on the *x*-axis and a scale of 1 cm to 1 litre on the *y*-axis.

Find from your graph
a the number of litres in the urn at
    (i) 2.15 p.m.   (ii) 5.15 p.m.   (iii) 3.45 p.m.   (iv) 4.45 p.m.
b the half-hour interval during which the most coffee was sold.
    How many litres was this?
    If each cup contains one-fifth of a litre, how many cups were needed?
c the number of litres of coffee sold altogether.

Straight line graphs

A straight line graph can be used to solve problems involving proportion.

Example 2

If 4 kg of tomatoes cost £3.20, draw a graph to find

a the cost of $1\frac{1}{2}$ kg of tomatoes
b the cost of $3\frac{1}{2}$ kg of tomatoes.

Find the weight of tomatoes that could be bought for

c £2   **d** £2.40

Use a horizontal scale of 2 cm to 1 kg and a vertical scale of 1 cm to 40 p.

Follow these steps

1 Find two more points on the graph by calculating the cost of 0 kg and the cost of 2 kg of tomatoes; then tabulate the results.

weight (kg)	0	0	4
cost (p)	0	160	320

2 Draw the axes, label them, and put in the scale.
3 Plot the graph using the table of values. Join up the points with a straight line.
4 Answer the questions.

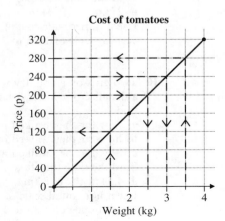

Cost of tomatoes

Answers

a $1\frac{1}{2}$ kg cost £1.20

b $3\frac{1}{2}$ kg cost £2.80

c £2 buys $2\frac{1}{2}$ kg

d £2.40 buys 3 kg

Exercise 4.2

1 If 4 kg of pears cost £1.60, draw a graph to find
  a the cost of 3 kg of pears
  b the cost of 5 kg of pears
  c the cost of $\frac{1}{2}$ kg of pears
  Find the weight of pears that could be bought for
  d £2.40   **e** £1   **f** £1.80
  Use a horizontal scale of 2 cm to 1 kg and a
  vertical scale of 1 cm to 10 p.

2 If 10 litres of paraffin cost £2, draw a graph to
  find
  a the cost of 4 litres
  b the cost of 9 litres
  c the cost of 17 litres
  d the cost of 11.5 litres

  Find the number of litres of paraffin that could
  be bought for
  e 60 p   **f** £1.40   **g** £2.60   **h** £3.10
  Use a horizontal scale of 1 cm to 1 litre and a
  vertical scale of 1 cm to 20 p.

3 If 40 litres of petrol cost £22 draw a graph to find
  a the cost of 30 litres of petrol
  b the cost of 50 litres of petrol
  c the cost of 45 litres of petrol
  Find the number of litres of petrol that can be
  bought for
  d £6   **e** £12.50   **f** £17.50
  Use a horizontal scale of 1 cm to 2 litres and a
  vertical scale of 1 cm to £1.

4 If 24 m² of floor covering costs £36, draw a graph
  to find
  a the cost of 4 m²
  b the cost of 10 m²
  c the cost of 18 m²
  Find the area of floor covering that can be
  bought for
  d £9   **e** £30   **f** £21
  Use a horizontal scale of 1 cm to 1 m² and a
  vertical scale of 1 cm to £2.

5 If 20 m² of carpet costs £120, draw a graph to
  find
  a the cost of 15 m² of carpet
  b the cost of 25 m² of carpet
  c the cost of 17.5 m² of carpet
  Find the area of carpet that can be bought for
  d £30   **e** £135   **f** £45
  Use a horizontal scale of 1 cm to 1 m² and a
  vertical scale of 1 cm to £10.

6 If the charge for a long-distance telephone call
  lasting 20 minutes is 60 p, draw a graph to find
  a the cost of a 30 minute call
  b the cost of a 25 minute call
  c the cost of a 35 minute call
  Find the time of a telephone call which costs
  d 45 p   **e** 24 p   **f** 84 p
  Use a horizontal scale of 1 cm to 2 min and a
  vertical scale of 1 cm to 5 p.

7 If 24 eggs cost £1.44, draw a graph to find
  a the cost of 30 eggs
  b the cost of 18 eggs
  Find the number of eggs which can be bought for
  c £2.16   **d** 36 p
  Use a horizontal scale of 1 cm to 2 eggs and a
  vertical scale of 1 cm to 10 p.

8 A woman driving her car along a motorway
  covers 160 km after 2 hours.
  Draw a graph to find
  a the distance covered after 3 h
  b the distance covered after $2\frac{1}{2}$ h
  c the distance covered after $3\frac{1}{2}$ h
  Find the time she takes to travel
  d 320 km   **e** 120 km   **f** 40 km
  Use a horizontal scale of 4 cm to 1 hour and a
  vertical scale of 1 cm to 20 km.

9 A boy cycles along a main road and covers 36 km
  after 2 hours. Draw a graph to find
  a the distance covered after 3 h
  b the distance covered after $2\frac{1}{2}$ h
  c the distance covered after 2 h 20 min
  d the distance covered after 40 min
  Find the time he takes to travel
  e 27 km   **f** 9 km   **g** 24 km   **h** 30 km
  Use a horizontal scale of 6 cm to 1 hour and a
  vertical scale of 1 cm to 2 km.

10 Two girls on a country walk find that they cover
  a distance of 6 km in 1 hour. Draw a graph to
  find
  a how far they walked in $1\frac{1}{2}$ h
  b how far they walked in 1 h 15 min
  c how far they walked in 40 min
  Find the time they take to walk
  d 4.5 km   **e** 8 km   **f** 2 km
  Use a horizontal scale of 12 cm to 1 hour and a
  vertical scale of 2 cm to 1 km.

Example 3

If a speed of 50 miles per hour (mph) is equal to 80 kilometres per hour, draw a graph to convert

a 45 mph to $km\,h^{-1}$ **c** 10 mph to $km\,h^{-1}$
b 48 $km\,h^{-1}$ to mph   **d** 64 $km\,h^{-1}$ to mph

Use a horizontal scale of 1 cm to 10 mph and a vertical scale of 1 cm to 10 $km\,h^{-1}$.

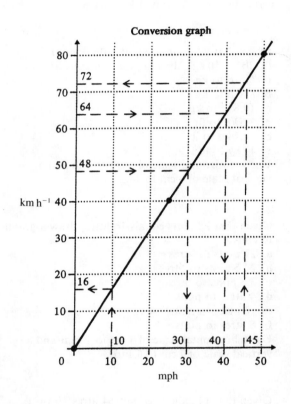

Conversion graph

Follow these steps

1 Find two more points on the graph by converting 0 mph and 25 mph to kilometres per hour; then tabulate the results.

speed (mph)	0	25	50
speed ($km\,h^{-1}$)	0	40	80

2 Draw the axes, label them and put in the scale.

3 Plot the graph using the above table of values, then join up the points with a straight line.

4 Answer the questions.

Answers

a 45 mph equals 72 $km\,h^{-1}$
b 48 $km\,h^{-1}$ equals 30 mph
c 10 mph equals 16 $km\,h^{-1}$
d 64 $km\,h^{-1}$ equals 40 mph

Exercise 4.3

1 Given that 10 miles equals 16 kilometres, draw a graph to convert
   a 15 miles to km
   b 2.5 miles to km
   c 12 km to miles
   d 20 km to miles
   Use a horizontal scale of 1 cm to 1 mile and a vertical scale of 1 cm to 1 kilometre.

2 Given that 22 pounds equals 10 kilograms (22 lb = 10 kg), draw a graph to convert
   a 5.5 lb to kg
   b 8.8 lb to kg
   c 19.8 lb to kg
   d 7.5 kg to lb
   e 12.5 kg to lb
   f 11 kg to lb
   Use a horizontal scale of 1 cm to 1 lb and a vertical scale of 1 cm to 1 kg.

3 Given that 28 pints equals 16 litres, draw a graph to convert
   a 21 pints to litres
   b 24.5 pints to litres
   c 3.5 pints to litres
   d 4 litres to pints
   e 10 litres to pints
   f 6 litres to pints
   Use a horizontal scale of 1 cm to 1 pint and a vertical scale of 1 cm to 1 litre.

4 Given that 14 gallons equals 64 litres, draw a graph to convert
   a 10.5 gallons to litres
   b 17.5 gallons to litres
   c 16 litres to gallons
   Use a horizontal scale of 1 cm to 1 gallon and a vertical scale of 1 cm to 5 litres.

5 Given that £8 = $18, draw a graph to convert
   a £12 to dollars
   b £2 to dollars
   c $13.5 to pounds
   d $22.5 to pounds
   Use a horizontal scale of 1 cm to £1 and a vertical scale of 1 cm to $1.

6 Given that £10 = FF 90, draw a graph to convert
   a £3 to francs
   b £4 to francs
   c £7 to francs
   d FF 54 to pounds
   e FF 72 to pounds
   f FF 81 to pounds
   Use a horizontal scale of 2 cm to £1 and a vertical scale of 1 cm to FF 5.

7 Given that £20 = DM 76, draw a graph to convert
   a £15 to marks
   b £12.50 to marks
   c DM 19 to pounds
   d DM 28.50 to pounds
   Use a horizontal scale of 1 cm to £1 and a vertical scale of 1 cm to DM 5.

8 Given that $10 \, cm^3$ of steel weighs 80 g, draw a graph to find
   a the weight of $7.5 \, cm^3$ of steel
   b the weight of $6 \, cm^3$ of steel
   c the weight of $4 \, cm^3$ of steel
   d the volume of 88 g of steel
   e the volume of 64 g of steel
   f the volume of 20 g of steel
   Use a horizontal scale of 2 cm to $1 \, cm^3$ and a vertical axis of 1 cm to 5 g.

9 Given that 20 litres of paraffin weighs 16 kg, draw a graph to find
   a the weight of 15 litres
   b the weight of 22.5 litres
   c the weight of 7.5 litres
   d the weight of 12.5 litres
   e the volume of 4 kg
   f the volume of 14 kg
   g the volume of 6.4 kg
   h the volume of 11.2 kg
   Use a horizontal scale of 1 cm to 1 litre and a vertical scale of 1 cm to 1 kg.

10 Given that 4 m of one type of electric wire weighs 280 g, draw a graph to find
   a the weight of 3 m of the wire
   b the weight of 3.5 m of the wire
   c the weight of 0.5 m of the wire
   d the length of 70 g of the wire
   e the length of 105 g of the wire
   f the length of 175 g of the wire
   Use a horizontal scale of 4 cm to 1 m and a vertical scale of 1 cm to 10 g.

Travel graphs

Example 4

The graph shows the journey of a car travelling at a steady speed of 40 km h^{-1} from Brighton to Portsmouth.

a Name the place where the car is
  (i) after 30 min
  (ii) after 1 h 15 min

b Find the time when the car is
  (i) at Chichester
  (ii) at Havant
  (iii) at Portsmouth

a (i) Worthing
  (ii) Bognor Regis

b (i) 13.30 h
  (ii) 14.00 h
  (iii) 14.15 h

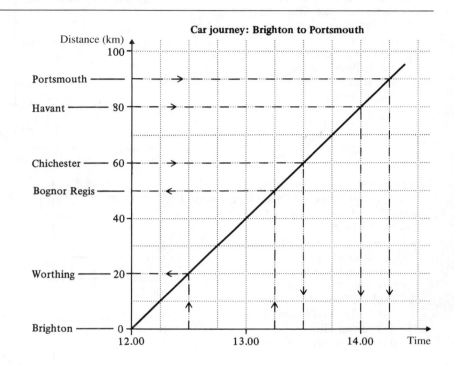

Exercise 4.4

1 The graph opposite shows the journey of a train travelling at a steady speed of 120 km h^{-1} from London (Paddington) to Cardiff.
  a Name the place where the train is
    (i) after 30 min   (ii) after 45 min
    (iii) after 1 h 30 min   (iv) after 1 h 45 min
  b Find the time when the train is
    (i) at Slough   (ii) at Swindon
    (iii) at Cardiff

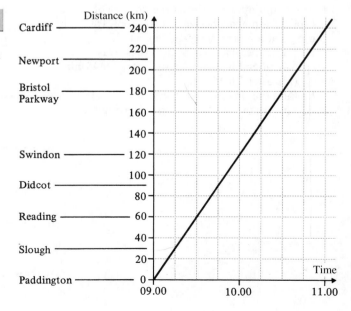

2 The graph opposite shows the journey of a car travelling at a steady speed of 80 km h^{-1} from Doncaster to Durham.

a Name the place where the car is
  (i) after 1 h   (ii) after 1 h 15 min
  (iii) after 2 h

b Find the time when the car is
  (i) at Bramham Moor
  (ii) at Scotch Corner
  (iii) at Aycliffe

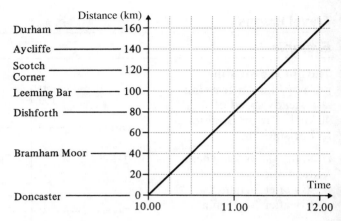

3 The graph opposite shows the details of a hike through Cannock Chase by a group of school children who walked at a steady speed of 4 km h^{-1}.

a Name the place where the group was
  (i) after 15 min
  (ii) after 1 h 15 min
  (iii) after 2 h 30 min

b Find the time when the group was
  (i) at The Old Pump House
  (ii) at Oat Hill
  (iii) at Shugborough Park Gates

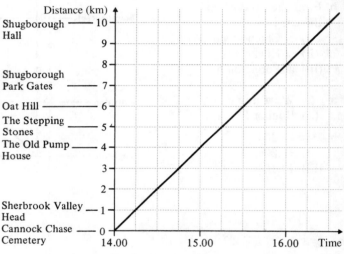

4 The graph opposite shows the journey of a cyclist from Manchester to Liverpool. He cycled at a steady speed of 24 km h^{-1}.

a Name the place where the cyclist was
  (i) after 1 h 30 min   (ii) after 1 h 45 min
  (iii) after 2 h 15 min

b Find the time when the cyclist reached
  (i) Irlam   (ii) Warrington

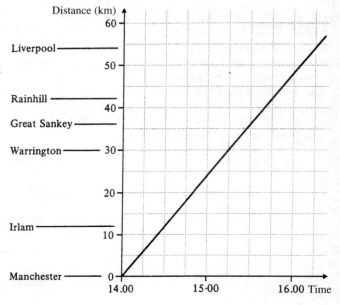

5 The graph opposite shows the journey of a
bus travelling at a steady speed of 32 km h^{-1}
from Newcastle to Berwick-on-Tweed.
  a Name the place where the bus is
    (i) after 30 min   (ii) after 45 min
    (iii) after 1 h 45 min   (iv) after 2 h 15 min
    (v) after 3 h 15 min
  b Find the time when the bus is
    (i) at Felton
    (ii) at Newton-on-the Moor
    (iii) at Belford
    (vi) at Fenwick

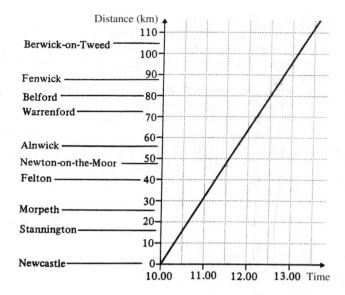

Example 5

The graph opposite shows a cyclist's
journey from Scunthorpe to Cleethorpes
and back.
a When did he reach Brigg?
b When did he leave Brigg?
c How far is Cleethorpes from Brigg?
d How long did he stop in Cleethorpes?
e What was his average speed on the
return journey?

a He reached Brigg at 09.30 h
b He left Brigg at 10.00 h
c The distance from Brigg to Cleethorpes is (50 − 10) km = 40 km
d He arrived in Cleethorpes at 12.00 h; he left at 15.00 h
Therefore, time spent in Cleethorpes = 3 h
e The return journey took $2\frac{1}{2}$ h; the distance is 50 km.

$$\therefore \quad \text{average speed} = \frac{\text{distance}}{\text{time}} = \frac{50}{2\frac{1}{2}} = 20 \text{ km h}^{-1}$$

Exercise 4.5

1 The graph opposite shows the return journey of a lorry driver from Birmingham to Bristol.
   a When did he reach Cheltenham?
   b When did he leave Cheltenham?
   c What is the distance from Cheltenham to Bristol?
   d How long did he stop in Bristol?
   e What was his average speed on the return journey?

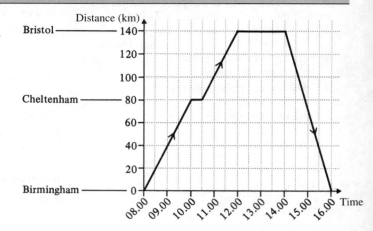

2 The graph opposite shows a day's walk by a group of hikers from Grasmere to the top of Helvellyn and back.
   a When did they reach Grisedale Tarn?
   b When did they set off again from Grisedale Tarn?
   c How long did they stop at the top of Helvellyn?
   d What was their average speed on the return journey?

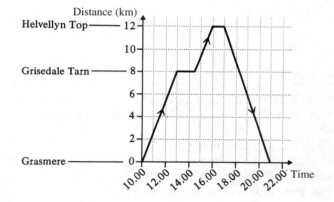

3 The graph opposite shows a man's car journey from Hull to Newcastle and back.
   a When did he reach York?
   b When did he leave York?
   c How far is it from York to Newcastle?
   d What was his average speed on the return journey?

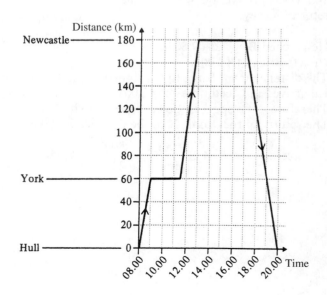

4 The return journey by train from Liverpool
   to York is shown in the graph opposite. It
   involved changing trains at Leeds on the
   outward journey.
   a When did the train arrive at Leeds?
   b When did the second train leave Leeds?
   c How long was the stay in York?
   d Find the average speed of the return
      journey.

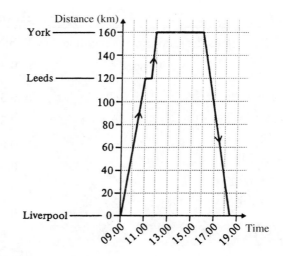

5 The graph shows a woman's return journey
   from London to Peterborough. On the
   way back she stopped in Hitchin to meet a
   friend.
   a Find the average speed of her outward
      journey.
   b How long did she stop in Peterborough?
   c What is the distance from Peterborough
      to Hitchin?
   d When did she reach Hitchin?
   e When did she leave Hitchin?
   f What was the average speed of her
      journey back from Hitchin to London?

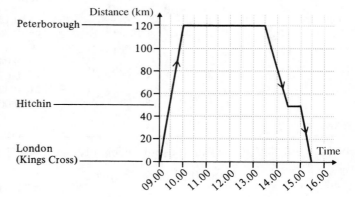

Unit 5 Percentages

Example 1

Write the following as decimals and percentages.

a $\frac{1}{4}$ **b** $\frac{3}{50}$ **c** $\frac{5}{8}$

a $\frac{1}{4} = 1 \div 4 = 0.25$
$\quad\quad = 0.25 \times 100\% = 25\%$

b $\frac{3}{50} = 3 \div 50 = 0.06$
$\quad\quad = 0.06 \times 100\% = 6\%$

c $\frac{5}{8} = 5 \div 8 = 0.625$
$\quad\quad = 0.625 \times 100\% = 62.5\%$

Exercise 5.1

Write the following as decimals and percentages.

1 $\frac{3}{10}$	**2** $\frac{9}{10}$	**3** $\frac{1}{10}$	**4** $\frac{3}{5}$	**5** $\frac{1}{5}$
6 $\frac{7}{50}$	**7** $\frac{11}{50}$	**8** $\frac{17}{50}$	**9** $\frac{29}{50}$	**10** $\frac{3}{20}$
11 $\frac{7}{20}$	**12** $\frac{1}{20}$	**13** $\frac{11}{20}$	**14** $\frac{9}{25}$	**15** $\frac{12}{25}$
16 $\frac{1}{8}$	**17** $\frac{1}{9}$	**18** $\frac{1}{6}$	**19** $\frac{7}{15}$	**20** $\frac{11}{15}$
21 $\frac{14}{15}$	**22** $\frac{13}{15}$	**23** $\frac{5}{12}$	**24** $\frac{31}{40}$	**25** $\frac{23}{40}$

Example 2

Write the following as fractions and decimals.

$$57\% = \frac{57}{100} = \begin{cases} 0.57 \text{ (as a decimal)} \\ \frac{57}{100} \text{ (as a fraction)} \end{cases}$$

$$18\% = \frac{18}{100} = \begin{cases} 0.18 \text{ (as a decimal)} \\ \frac{9}{50} \text{ (as a fraction)} \end{cases}$$

$$35\% = \frac{35}{100} = \begin{cases} 0.35 \text{ (as a decimal)} \\ \frac{7}{20} \text{ (as a fraction)} \end{cases}$$

Exercise 5.2

Write the following as fractions and decimals.

1 3%	**2** 11%	**3** 39%	**4** 53%
5 81%	**6** 42%	**7** 38%	**8** 86%
9 45%	**10** 65%	**11** 32%	**12** 56%
13 4%	**14** 90%	**15** 20%	**16** 18%
17 26%	**18** 37%	**19** 41%	**20** 67%
21 84%	**22** 80%	**23** 60%	**24** 30%
25 10%			

Example 3

Write the following as fractions and percentages.

a 0.32   **b** 0.07   **c** 0.375

a $0.32 = \frac{32}{100} = \frac{8}{25}$
$\quad 0.32 = 0.32 \times 100\% = 32\%$

b $0.07 = \frac{7}{100}$
$\quad 0.07 = 0.07 \times 100\% = 7\%$

c $0.375 = \frac{375}{1000} = \frac{3}{8}$
$\quad 0.375 = 0.375 \times 100\% = 37.5\%$

Exercise 5.3

Write the following as fractions and percentages.

1 0.15	**2** 0.29	**3** 0.48	**4** 0.53
5 0.76	**6** 0.93	**7** 0.9	**8** 0.7
9 0.4	**10** 0.2	**11** 0.09	**12** 0.06
13 0.04	**14** 0.625	**15** 0.575	**16** 0.225
17 0.075	**18** 0.015	**19** 0.2625	**20** 0.8125
21 0.4375	**22** 0.0625	**23** 0.025	**24** 0.01
25 0.001			

Calculating a fraction of a number requires a combination of multiplication and division.

Example 4

Find

a $\frac{1}{2}$ of 144   **b** $\frac{1}{5}$ of 34

c $\frac{3}{4}$ of 68   **d** $\frac{5}{8}$ of 68

a $\frac{1}{2}$ of $144 = 144 \div 2 = 72$

b $\frac{1}{5}$ of $34 = 34 \div 5 = 6.8$

c $\frac{3}{4}$ of $68 = (68 \div 4) \times 3 = 17 \times 3 = 51$

d $\frac{5}{8}$ of $68 = (68 \div 8) \times 5 = 8.5 \times 5 = 42.5$

Exercise 5.4

Find

1 $\frac{1}{2}$ of 46	**2** $\frac{1}{3}$ of 99	**3** $\frac{1}{4}$ of 64
4 $\frac{1}{5}$ of 1000	**5** $\frac{1}{9}$ of 72	**6** $\frac{2}{3}$ of 330
7 $\frac{3}{4}$ of 224	**8** $\frac{2}{5}$ of 115	**9** $\frac{5}{6}$ of 30

10 $\frac{1}{7}$ of 700   **11** $\frac{1}{8}$ of 800   **12** $\frac{3}{8}$ of 800

13 $\frac{2}{9}$ of 900   **14** $\frac{6}{7}$ of 350   **15** $\frac{3}{5}$ of 80

16 $\frac{3}{5}$ of 8   **17** $\frac{7}{8}$ of 16   **18** $\frac{7}{8}$ of 8

19 $\frac{7}{8}$ of 4   **20** $\frac{8}{9}$ of 90   **21** $\frac{8}{9}$ of 9

22 $\frac{8}{9}$ of 1   **23** $\frac{5}{7}$ of 24.5   **24** $\frac{4}{7}$ of 56

25 $\frac{4}{7}$ of 5.6   **26** $\frac{7}{9}$ of 40.5   **27** $\frac{4}{5}$ of 12

28 $\frac{5}{9}$ of 243   **29** $\frac{5}{8}$ of 244   **30** $\frac{4}{9}$ of 9999

31 $\frac{3}{7}$ of 8.4   **32** $\frac{2}{7}$ of 84   **33** $\frac{5}{13}$ of 26

34 $\frac{5}{13}$ of 2600   **35** $\frac{7}{19}$ of 38   **36** $\frac{7}{19}$ of 3.8

37 $\frac{75}{100}$ of 80   **38** $\frac{60}{100}$ of 220   **39** $\frac{90}{100}$ of 340

40 $\frac{44}{100}$ of 625

Example 5

There are 24 000 spectators at a football match and police estimate that $\frac{7}{8}$ of them support the home team.

How many home supporters does this statement represent?

$$\frac{7}{8} \text{ of } 24\,000 = (24\,000 \div 8) \times 7 = 21\,000$$

Therefore, there are 21 000 home supporters.

Exercise 5.5

1 There are 144 apples in a box.
Calculate how many apples each statement represents.
   a $\frac{1}{2}$ of the apples are red.
   b $\frac{3}{4}$ of the apples are French.
   c $\frac{5}{12}$ of the apples weigh more than 110 grams.
   d $\frac{5}{36}$ of the apples are bad.
   e $\frac{1}{6}$ of the apples are in top layer.

2 There are 260 girls and 240 boys in a school.
Calculate how many pupils each statement represents.
   a $\frac{2}{5}$ of the girls come to school by bike.
   b $\frac{3}{10}$ of the boys stay to school dinner.
   c $\frac{7}{10}$ of the girls wear earrings.
   d All the boys and $\frac{1}{5}$ of the girls wear ties.
   e $\frac{3}{10}$ of the girls and $\frac{4}{10}$ of the boys play for a school team.
   f $\frac{81}{100}$ of the pupils live within two miles of the school.
   g $\frac{11}{100}$ of the pupils wear glasses.
   h $\frac{33}{100}$ of the pupils are left handed.
   i $\frac{19}{100}$ of the pupils are in Year 7.
   j $\frac{21}{100}$ of the pupils are in Year 10.

3 A farmer has a flock of 300 sheep.

Calculate how many sheep each statement represents.
   a $\frac{2}{25}$ of the sheep are black.
   b $\frac{5}{12}$ of the sheep are lambs.
   c $\frac{7}{30}$ of the sheep are in the North Field.
   d $\frac{3}{20}$ of the sheep are in the West Field.
   e $\frac{7}{10}$ of the sheep have been dipped.
   f $\frac{31}{100}$ of the sheep are over two years old.
   g $\frac{83}{100}$ of the sheep are ewes (females).
   h The vet saw $\frac{7}{100}$ of the sheep last month.
   i $\frac{19}{100}$ of the sheep will be sold next week.
   j $\frac{41}{100}$ of the sheep have been shorn.

4 There are 240 marks available in a Mathematics examination with three papers, Paper 1, Paper 2 and Paper 3.

Calculate how many marks each statement represents.

a Amy scored $\frac{3}{8}$ of the available marks.

b Janice scored $\frac{5}{6}$ of the available marks.

c Siloben scored $\frac{29}{30}$ of the available marks.

d $\frac{25}{100}$ of the marks are for algebra questions.

e $\frac{20}{100}$ of the marks are for geometry questions.

f $\frac{40}{100}$ of the marks are for arithmetic questions.

g $\frac{30}{100}$ of the marks are for Paper 1.

h $\frac{55}{100}$ of the marks are for Paper 2.

i $\frac{15}{100}$ of the marks are for Paper 3.

j $\frac{95}{100}$ or more of the marks are needed for a pass with distinction.

A percentage of a quantity can be found by changing the percentage into a fraction and calculating this fraction of the quantity.

Example 6

Find

a 15% of £500   b 66% of 250 g

c $12\frac{1}{2}$% of 160 cm

a $15\% = \frac{15}{100}$

$\frac{15}{100}$ of £500 = (£500 ÷ 100) × 15 = £75

b $66\% = \frac{66}{100}$

$\frac{66}{100}$ of 250 g = (250 g ÷ 100) × 66 = 165 g

c $12\frac{1}{2}\% = \frac{12\frac{1}{2}}{100}$

This is not a simple fraction so we multiply top and bottom by 2 to remove the $\frac{1}{2}$.

$$\frac{12\frac{1}{2}}{100} \xrightarrow{\times 2} = \frac{25}{200} \xleftarrow{\times 2}$$

$\frac{25}{200}$ of 160 cm = (160 cm ÷ 200) × 25

$= 20$ cm

Exercise 5.6

Find

1 8% of £500	2 5% of £900
3 6% of 400 g	4 3% of £1200
5 20% of £60	6 60% of £90
7 50% of 30 cm	8 40% of £120
9 80% of £110	10 40% of £25
11 60% of £15	12 20% of 75 cm
13 80% of 35 cm	14 25% of £96
15 75% of £28	16 75% of £64
17 35% of £60	18 45% of 80 cm
19 15% of 120 g	20 40% of £1.50
21 60% of £1.20	22 80% of 1 m 10 cm
23 20% of £3.50	24 60% of £2.50
25 40% of £3.20	26 25% of £1.80
27 75% of 1 m 20 cm	28 75% of 1 kg
29 $12\frac{1}{2}$% of £72	30 $12\frac{1}{2}$% of £4.80

One quantity can be written as a percentage of another quantity, provided each quantity is written in the same units.

First write one quantity as a fraction of the other. Then change this fraction to a percentage.

Example 7

Find

a 10 cm as a percentage of 50 cm

b £1.50 as a percentage of £5

c 250 g as a percentage of 2 kg.

a 10 as a fraction of $50 = \frac{10}{50}$

$10 ÷ 50 = 0.2$

$0.2 × 100\% = 20\%$

b £1.5 as a fraction of £5.00 $= \frac{1.5}{5.00}$

$1.5 ÷ 5.00 = 0.3$

$0.3 × 100\% = 30\%$

c 250 g as a fraction of 2 kg $= \frac{250}{2000}$

$250 ÷ 2000 = 0.125$

$0.125 × 100\% = 12.5\%$

Exercise 5.7

Find

1 £72 as a percentage of £800
2 £42 as a percentage of £600
3 56 g as a percentage of 700 g
4 £66 as a percentage of £1100
5 £35 as a percentage of £50
6 £27 as a percentage of £90
7 £54 as a percentage of £60
8 32 cm as a percentage of 80 cm
9 24 cm as a percentage of 30 cm
10 £45 as a percentage of £75
11 £18 as a percentage of £45
12 £100 as a percentage of £125
13 £21 as a percentage of £105
14 £28 as a percentage of £80
15 66 g as a percentage of 120 g
16 £24 as a percentage of £160
17 27 cm as a percentage of 60 cm
18 54 cm as a percentage of 72 cm
19 £27 as a percentage of £108
20 £1.20 as a percentage of £1.50
21 £1.40 as a percentage of £3.50
22 1 m 44 cm as a percentage of 2 m 40 cm
23 £2 as a percentage of £2.50
24 72 p as a percentage of £1.80
25 96 p as a percentage of £1.20
26 84 p as a percentage of £1.40
27 54 cm as a percentage of 2 m 70 cm
28 35 p as a percentage of £1.40
29 £1.80 as a percentage of £2.40
30 50 cm as a percentage of 4 m

Example 8

In a school of 1400 pupils, 45% of them are boys.

Find

a the number of boys in the school
b the percentage of the pupils who stay for lunch if 770 of them do so.

a Number of boys = 45% of 1400

$45\% = \frac{45}{100}$

$\frac{45}{100}$ of 1400 = (1400 ÷ 100) × 15 = 630

b Fraction who stay = $\frac{770}{1400}$

770 ÷ 1400 = 0.55

0.55 × 100% = 55%

Exercise 5.8

1 A football club has 25 players, but only 60% of them have ever played for the first team.
Find the number who have played for the first team.

2 It takes me 45 minutes to get to school and I spend 80% of that time travelling on the bus.
How long does my bus journey last?

3 A room has an area of 30 m² and a carpet covers 90% of this area.
Find the area of the carpet.

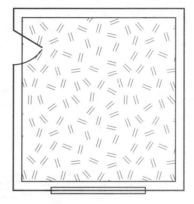

4 A farmer has 40 sheep and 35% of them are black.
Find the number of black sheep.

5 A car's petrol tank can hold 36 litres.
How many litres are there in it if it is 75% full?

6 There are 32 boys in class 5A and one day $12\frac{1}{2}\%$ of them are absent.
Find the number who are absent.

7 At 3 p.m. a newspaper seller is given 350 papers and by 5 p.m. she has sold 40% of them.
Find the number that she has sold by 5 p.m.

8 A match box had 50 matches inside when it was bought, but only 70% of them are left. How many matches have been used?

9 There are 20 boys in class 1B and they have three sports options to choose from. If 25% choose athletics, 35% choose swimming and 40% choose cricket, find the number who choose each of the three sports.

10 At Northgate School there are 750 pupils. The percentage absent on each day of a certain week is shown below.

Monday	8%	Thursday	2%
Tuesday	10%	Friday	4%
Wednesday	6%		

Find the number absent on each day.

11 There are 20 eggs in a fridge and 6 of them are brown. Find the percentage which are brown.

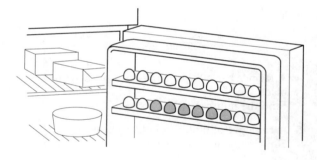

12 A passage has an area of 25 m² and there is a carpet on its floor which has an area of 20 m². What percentage of the floor's area is covered by the carpet?

13 An examination is marked out of 120 and one girl gets 84 marks. Find her mark as a percentage.

14 60 pupils are entered for an examination and 45 of them pass. Find the percentage who pass.

15 A factory employs 160 workers and 72 of them travel to work by bus. Find the percentage who use the bus.

16 There are 24 girls in class 2B and one day 18 of them are present. Find the percentage who are present.

17 At a football match a programme seller is supplied with 1200 programmes and he sells 1080. What percentage of them does he sell?

18 10 m of wood is bought to make the window frame illustrated. What percentage of the wood is used?

←260 cm→
140 cm   140 cm
←260 cm→

19 There are 30 girls in class 4C and they have four sports options to choose from. If 12 choose tennis, 9 choose swimming, 3 choose rounders and 6 choose athletics, find the percentage who choose each sport.

20 At Manor Grange School there are 450 pupils. The number absent on each day of a certain week is shown below.

Monday	27	Thursday	36
Tuesday	18	Friday	54
Wednesday	45		

Find the percentage who are absent each day.

Unit 6   Angles

An angle is the way we measure turn or change of direction.

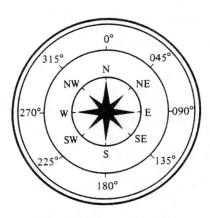

A complete turn is divided into 360 parts called degrees.

$$1 \text{ complete turn} = 360°$$

Example 1

Find the number of degrees of turn when the wind changes in a clockwise direction

a from N to E

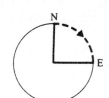

From N to E = 90°

b from NE to W

NE to E = 45°

E to W = 180°

So NE to W = 45° + 180°
         = 225°

c from NW to SE

NW to N = 45°
N to E   = 90°
E to SE   = 45°

So NW to SE = 45° + 90° + 45°
          = 180°

Exercise 6.1

Find the number of degrees of turn when the wind changes in a clockwise direction

1 from N to NE	**2** from N to Se
3 from N to S	**4** from N to W
5 from N to SW	**6** from E to S
7 from E to SE	**8** from E to SW
9 from S to W	**10** from S to NW
11 from S to E	**12** from W to E
13 from W to SE	**14** from NE to E
15 from NE to S	**16** from NE to SW
17 from SE to S	**18** from SE to N
19 from SW to N	**20** from NW to NE

Example 2

Find the size of the smaller angle between the hands of the clock when the clock is showing the following times.

a 9 o'clock

The angle is 90°

b 1 o'clock

The angle is one-third of 90° = 30°

c 8 o'clock

The angle = 90° + 30°
        = 120°

50

Exercise 6.2

Find the size of the smaller angle between the hands of a clock when the clock is showing the following times.

1	3 o'clock	**2**	11 o'clock
3	4 o'clock	**4**	10 o'clock
5	2 o'clock	**6**	6 o'clock
7	5 o'clock	**8**	7 o'clock

A quarter turn (90°) is called a *right angle*.

An angle that is less than 90° is called an *acute angle*.

An angle that is greater than 90° but less than 180° is called an *obtuse angle*.

An angle of 180° is called a *straight angle* because it is a straight line.

An angle that is greater than 180° is called a *reflex angle*.

Example 3

This weighing machine at the Post Office can weigh up to 300 grams.

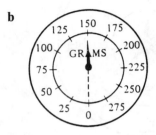

a Find the angle through which the pointer turns when weighing a letter of 50 g and state the type of angle.
b Find the angle through which the pointer turns when weighing a parcel of 150 g and state the type of angle.

a

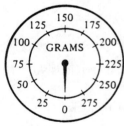

The pointer moves from 0 to 50.

This is $\frac{50}{300}$ of a complete turn.

$\therefore$ angle $= \frac{50}{300} \times 360° = 60°$

This is an acute angle.

b

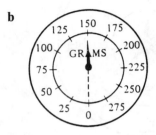

The pointer moves from 0 to 150.

This is $\frac{150}{300}$ of a complete turn.

$\therefore$ angle $= \frac{150}{300} \times 360° = 180°$

This is a straight angle.

Exercise 6.3

This weighing machine can weight up to 120 kg.

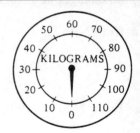

Peter weighs 60 kg.   Jodie weighs 40 kg.
Luke weighs 30 kg.   Annie weighs 20 kg.
Jodie's dog Patch weighs 10 kg.

Find the size of the angle through which the pointer turns when the following stand on the machine. State the type of angle.

1 Annie   **2** Patch   **3** Luke   **4** Jodie   **5** Peter
6 Annie and Patch together
7 Luke and Patch together
8 Jodie and Patch together
9 Jodie and Annie together
10 Luke and Annie together
11 Peter and Luke together
12 Peter and Patch together

For questions **13** and **14**, look at the picture below of the speedometer in the cab of a lorry.

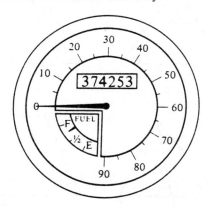

13 If the lorry starts off and accelerates up to 90 km h^{-1}, find the angle turned by the pointer when the speed has reached
  a 10 km h^{-1} **b** 15 km h^{-1} **c** 20 km h^{-1}
  d 30 km h^{-1} **e** 40 km h^{-1} **f** 45 km h^{-1}
  g 60 km h^{-1} **h** 90 km h^{-1}

14 The lorry now slows down.
  Find the angle through which the pointer has turned back when the speed has fallen from 90 km h^{-1} to
  a 80 km h^{-1} **b** 75 km h^{-1} **c** 70 km h^{-1}
  d 60 km h^{-1} **e** 50 km h^{-1} **f** 30 km h^{-1}

15 The pictures show the readings on a weather glass for each day of a certain week.

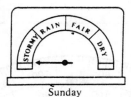
Sunday

Monday

Tuesday

Wednesday

Thursday

Friday

Saturday

Find the angle turned by the pointer between
  a Sunday and Tuesday
  b Sunday and Wednesday
  c Sunday and Friday
  d Tuesday and Wednesday
  e Tuesday and Friday
  f Wednesday and Friday
  g Friday and Saturday

Two angles whose sum is 90° are called *complementary* angles.
e.g. 20° is the complement of 70°

Two angles whose sum is 180° are called *supplementary* angles.
e.g. 20° is the supplement of 160°

Exercise 6.4

Find the complement of the following angles.

1 10°	**2** 30°	**3** 50°	**4** 15°
5 35°	**6** 45°	**7** 65°	**8** 85°
9 12°	**10** 36°	**11** 72°	**12** 66°
13 48$\frac{1}{2}$°	**14** 82$\frac{1}{2}$°	**15** 27.5°	

Find the supplement of the following angles.

16 30°	**17** 40°	**18** 60°	**19** 80°
20 90°	**21** 170°	**22** 130°	**23** 110°
24 5°	**25** 15°	**26** 45°	**27** 67$\frac{1}{2}$°
28 105°	**29** 155°	**30** 97.5°	

If two straight lines AB and AC meet at A as shown they form an acute angle BAC, which is written B$\hat{A}$C.

In the diagram, the two straight lines XY and XZ meet at X and form an obtuse angle Y$\hat{X}$Z.

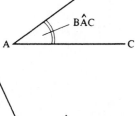

52

Example 4

Using three letters, name the angles marked
(i) *a*   (ii) *b*   (iii) *c*.

(i) $a = Q\widehat{R}S$
(ii) $b = P\widehat{M}S$
(iii) $c = Q\widehat{P}R$

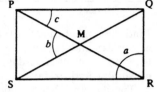

Exercise 6.5

Using three letters, name the marked angle or angles
in each of the following diagrams.

1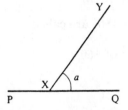

2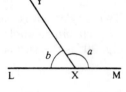

3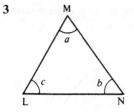

4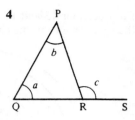

5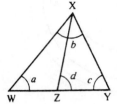

6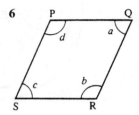

7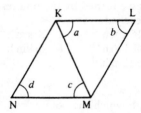

8

Using a protractor

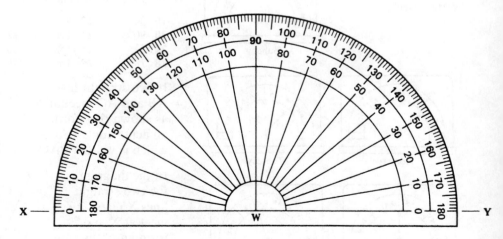

To measure an angle you need a protractor as shown above. XY shows the
base line and W the centre point.

Example 5

Measure the size of PQ̂R

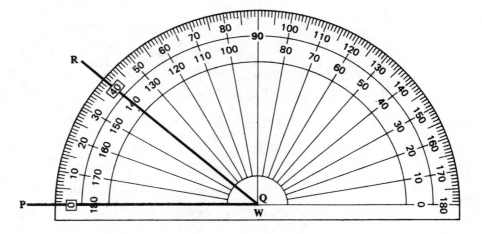

1 Place the protractor on the angle so that W is on Q as shown and WX lies on PQ.

2 Where the line QR cuts the scale, read off the angle on the scale starting from 0° at P.

3 PQ̂R = 40°.

Example 6

Measure the size of LM̂N

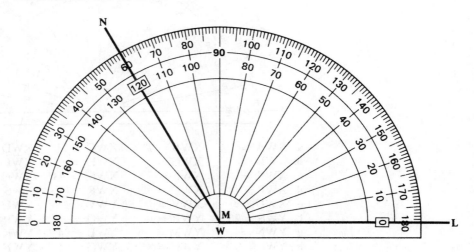

Place W on M and Y on L; from the inner scale, LM̂N = 120°.

Exercise 6.6

For each question look at the diagram, then copy and fill in the details below.

1

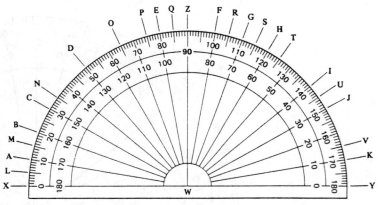

a $X\widehat{W}A = 10°$ $X\widehat{W}B = 20°$ $X\widehat{W}C =$ $X\widehat{W}D =$ $X\widehat{W}E =$
b $X\widehat{W}Z =$ $X\widehat{W}F = 100°$ $X\widehat{W}G = 110°$ $X\widehat{W}H =$ $X\widehat{W}I =$
c $X\widehat{W}J =$ $X\widehat{W}K =$ $X\widehat{W}Y =$ $X\widehat{W}L = 5°$ $X\widehat{W}M = 15°$
d $X\widehat{W}N =$ $X\widehat{W}O =$ $X\widehat{W}P =$ $X\widehat{W}Q =$ $X\widehat{W}R = 105°$
e $X\widehat{W}S = 115°$ $X\widehat{W}T =$ $X\widehat{W}U =$ $X\widehat{W}V =$ $Y\widehat{W}K = 10°$
f $Y\widehat{W}J = 30°$ $Y\widehat{W}I =$ $Y\widehat{W}H =$ $Y\widehat{W}G =$ $Y\widehat{W}F =$
g $Y\widehat{W}Z =$ $Y\widehat{W}E = 100°$ $Y\widehat{W}D =$ $Y\widehat{W}C =$ $Y\widehat{W}B =$
h $Y\widehat{W}A =$ $Y\widehat{W}X =$ $Y\widehat{W}V = 15°$ $Y\widehat{W}U = 35°$ $Y\widehat{W}T =$
i $Y\widehat{W}S =$ $Y\widehat{W}R =$ $Y\widehat{W}Q = 95°$ $Y\widehat{W}P = 105°$ $Y\widehat{W}O = 115°$
j $Y\widehat{W}N =$ $Y\widehat{W}M =$ $Y\widehat{W}L =$

2

a $X\widehat{W}A = 4°$ $X\widehat{W}B = 7°$ $X\widehat{W}C = 13°$ $X\widehat{W}D =$ $X\widehat{W}E = 22°$
b $X\widehat{W}F =$ $X\widehat{W}G =$ $X\widehat{W}H =$ $X\widehat{W}I =$ $X\widehat{W}J =$
c $X\widehat{W}K =$ $X\widehat{W}L =$ $X\widehat{W}M = 93°$ $X\widehat{W}N = 108°$ $X\widehat{W}O =$
d $X\widehat{W}P =$ $X\widehat{W}Q =$ $X\widehat{W}R =$ $X\widehat{W}S =$ $X\widehat{W}T =$
e $X\widehat{W}U =$ $X\widehat{W}V =$ $Y\widehat{W}V = 3°$ $Y\widehat{W}U =$ $Y\widehat{W}T = 18°$
f $Y\widehat{W}S = 23°$ $Y\widehat{W}R =$ $Y\widehat{W}Q =$ $Y\widehat{W}P =$ $Y\widehat{W}O =$
g $Y\widehat{W}N =$ $Y\widehat{W}M =$ $Y\widehat{W}L = 94°$ $Y\widehat{W}K = 106°$ $Y\widehat{W}J =$
h $Y\widehat{W}I =$ $Y\widehat{W}H =$ $Y\widehat{W}G =$ $Y\widehat{W}F =$ $Y\widehat{W}E =$
i $Y\widehat{W}D =$ $Y\widehat{W}C =$ $Y\widehat{W}B =$ $Y\widehat{W}A =$

Exercise 6.7

With a protractor, measure each of the following angles.

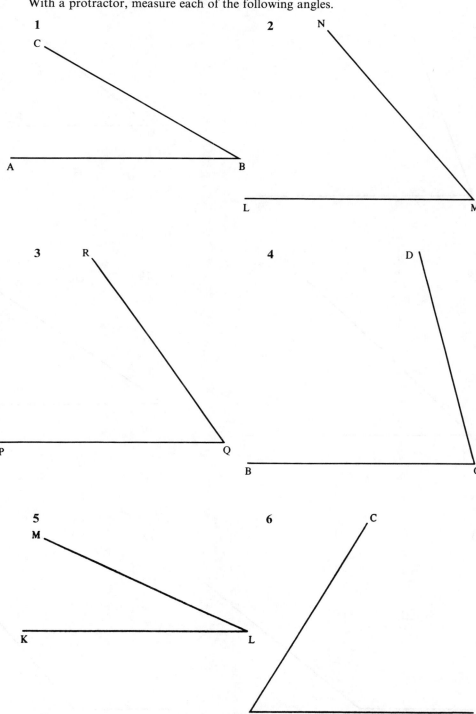

1

C

A   B

2

N

L   M

3

R

P   Q

4

D

B   C

5

M

K   L

6

C

B   A

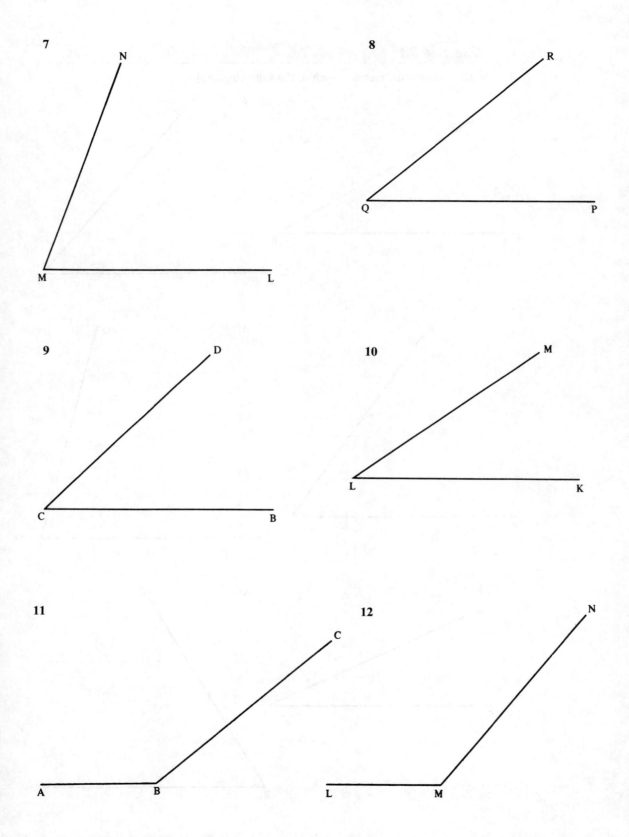

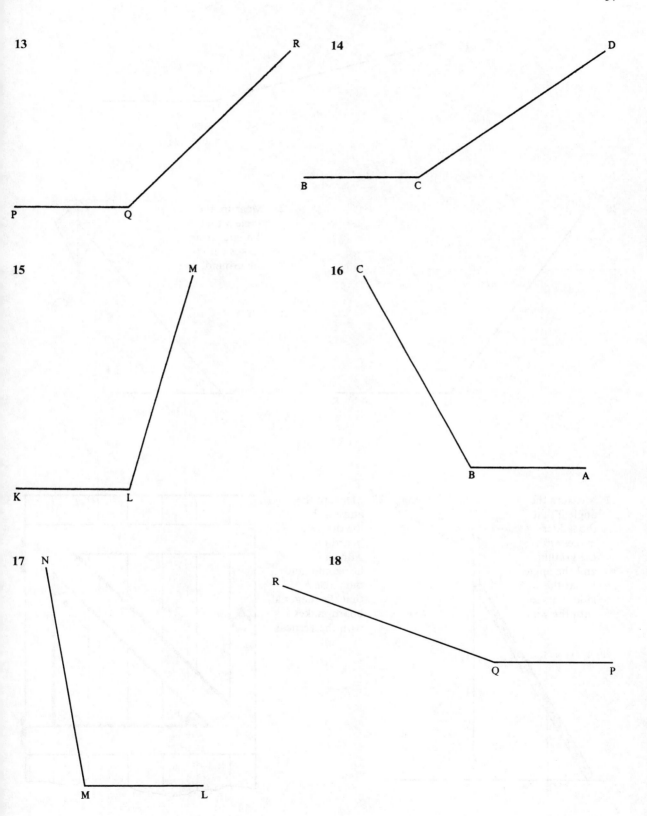

13

P   Q   R

14

B   C   D

15

K   L   M

16

C   B   A

17

N   M   L

18

R   Q   P

58

19

20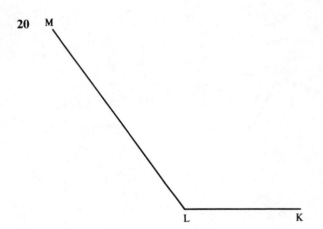

21 Measure the angle *a* that the kite string makes with the ground.

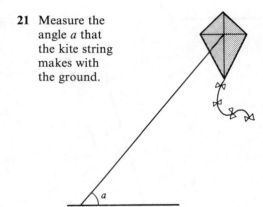

22 Measure the angle *a* that the ladder makes with the ground, and the angle *b* that the ladder makes with the wall.

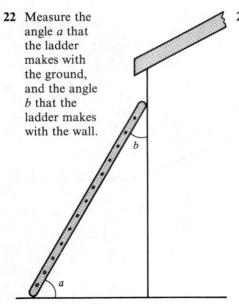

23 Measure the angle *a* that the diagonal board makes with the horizontal and the angle *b* that the diagonal board makes with the vertical.

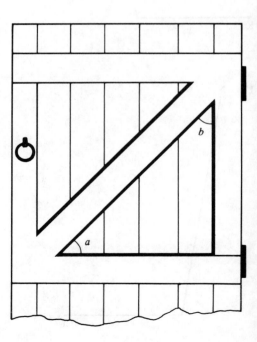

24 Measure the angle *a* between the two parts of the folding ruler.

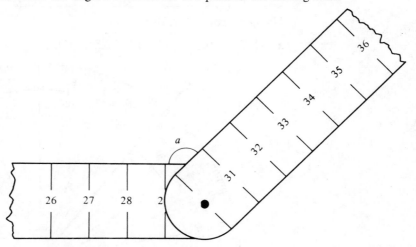

25 Measure the two angles *a* and *b* on the blade of this modelling knife.

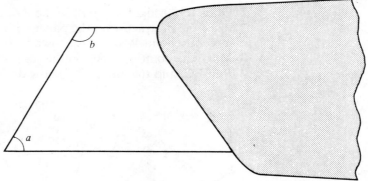

26 Measure the angle *a* between the wall and the slope of the roof, and the angle *b* between the two sloping parts of the roof.

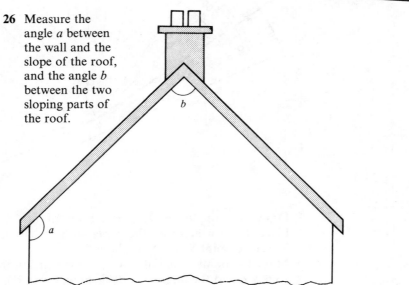

Example 7

Using a protractor, draw

a $\widehat{ABC} = 50°$,   **b** $\widehat{XYZ} = 170°$.

a

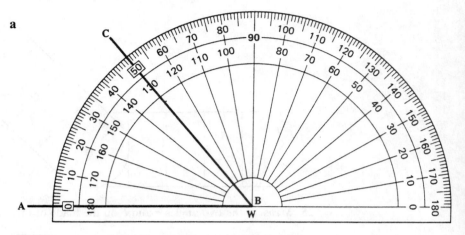

1 Draw the straight line AB. Make it 6 cm long.
2 Place the protractor on the paper with its base line on the line AB and its centre point W on B as shown.
3 Mark the point C at 50° on the scale starting from 0° at A.
4 Join BC, and the angle 50° is now drawn complete.

b

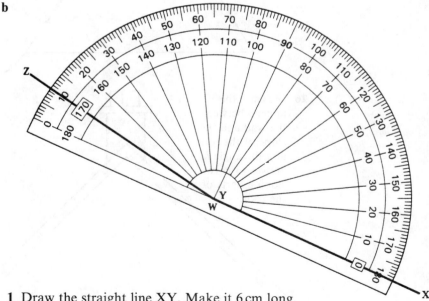

1 Draw the straight line XY. Make it 6 cm long.
2 Place the protractor on the paper with its base line on the line XY and its centre point W on Y as shown.
3 Mark the point Z at 170° on the scale starting from 0° at X.
4 Join YZ and the angle of 170° is now drawn complete.

Exercise 6.8

For each question, draw a line AB 6 cm long.
Then draw the angle.

1	$\widehat{ABC} = 60°$	**2**	$\widehat{ABC} = 40°$
3	$\widehat{ABC} = 45°$	**4**	$\widehat{ABC} = 65°$
5	$\widehat{ABC} = 35°$	**6**	$\widehat{BAC} = 30°$
7	$\widehat{BAC} = 80°$	**8**	$\widehat{BAC} = 50°$
9	$\widehat{BAC} = 55°$	**10**	$\widehat{BAC} = 25°$
11	$\widehat{ABC} = 120°$	**12**	$\widehat{ABC} = 150°$
13	$\widehat{ABC} = 155°$	**14**	$\widehat{ABC} = 125°$
15	$\widehat{ABC} = 115°$	**16**	$\widehat{BAC} = 130°$
17	$\widehat{BAC} = 110°$	**18**	$\widehat{BAC} = 140°$
19	$\widehat{BAC} = 145°$	**20**	$\widehat{BAC} = 95°$

An angle can be described with either three
letters or one letter.

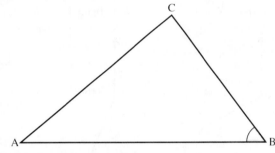

In the diagram the shaded angle can be
described as $\widehat{ABC}$ or as $\widehat{B}$.

Example 8

Draw a triangle ABC with AB = 5 cm, $\widehat{A} = 50°$
and $\widehat{B} = 70°$.
Measure the third angle with a protractor.

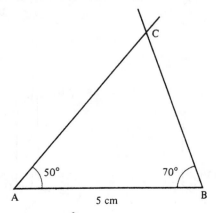

By measurement, $\widehat{C} = 60°$

Exercise 6.9

For each question, draw the triangle ABC from the
details given.
Then measure $\widehat{C}$ with a protractor.

1	AB = 5 cm,	$\widehat{A} = 40°$,	$\widehat{B} = 60°$
2	AB = 5 cm,	$\widehat{A} = 30°$,	$\widehat{B} = 80°$
3	AB = 5 cm,	$\widehat{A} = 50°$,	$\widehat{B} = 40°$
4	AB = 5 cm,	$\widehat{A} = 60°$,	$\widehat{B} = 90°$
5	AB = 5 cm,	$\widehat{A} = 50°$,	$\widehat{B} = 50°$
6	AB = 5 cm,	$\widehat{A} = 60°$,	$\widehat{B} = 60°$
7	AB = 6 cm,	$\widehat{A} = 30°$,	$\widehat{B} = 40°$
8	AB = 6 cm,	$\widehat{A} = 40°$,	$\widehat{B} = 40°$
9	AB = 6 cm,	$\widehat{A} = 50°$,	$\widehat{B} = 100°$
10	AB = 6 cm,	$\widehat{A} = 20°$,	$\widehat{B} = 110°$

Bearings

A bearing (or direction) is measured clockwise
from North.

For example

a

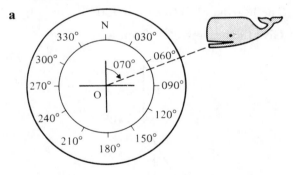

The whale has a bearing of 070° from O.

b

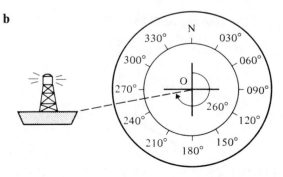

The lightship has a bearing of 260° from O.

Bearings are *always* given in three figures in order to avoid errors, e.g. 070°, and not 70°.

Remember that bearings are always measured *clockwise* from North.

Example 9

a Give the bearing of B from A.

The bearing of B from A is 040°

b Give the bearing of Q from P.

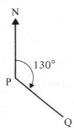

The bearing of Q from P is 130°

c Give the bearing of Y from X.

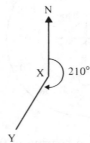

The bearing of Y from X is 210°

d Give the bearing of C from B.

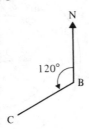

The bearing of C from B is
    360° − 120° = 240°

Exercise 6.10

Give the bearings of the following.

1 B from A

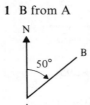

2 Q from P

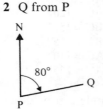

3 Y from X

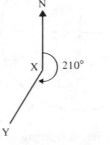

4 C from B

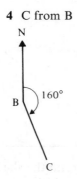

5 R from Q

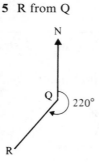

6 Z from Y

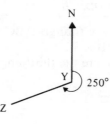

7 D from C

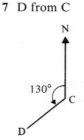

8 V from U

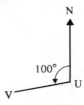

9 B from A

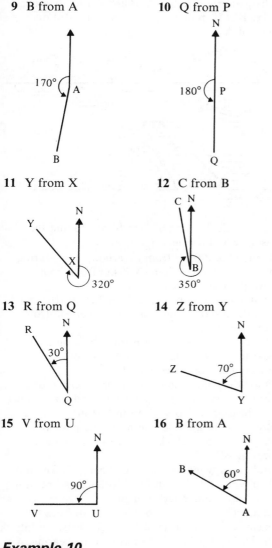

170° A

B

10 Q from P

N

180° P

Q

11 Y from X

Y

N

X

320°

12 C from B

C N

B

350°

13 R from Q

R N

30°

Q

14 Z from Y

N

Z

70°

Y

15 V from U

N

90°

V U

16 B from A

N

B

60°

A

1 Draw a vertical line through the point A to fix North.
2 With your protractor, draw N$\widehat{A}$X at 65° in the clockwise direction from the line AN.
3 Mark off point B 3 cm along the line AX.

Exercise 6.11

For each question draw a diagram to show the relative positions of the points. Use a scale of 1 cm to 1 km.

1 B is on a bearing of 030° from A and is 3 km from A.
2 Q is on a bearing of 070° from P and is 3 km from P.
3 Y is on a bearing of 045° from X and is 4 km from X.
4 C is on a bearing of 150° from B and is 4 km from B.
5 R is on a bearing of 135° from Q and is 5 km from Q.
6 Z is on a bearing of 200° from Y and is 5 km from Y.
7 D is on a bearing of 225° from C and is 3 km from C.
8 V is on a bearing of 300° from U and is 3 km from U.
9 B is on a bearing of 340° from A and is 4 km from A.
10 Q is on a bearing of 315° from P and is 4 km from P.

You can plot the course followed by a ship or an aeroplane if its distance and bearing at each change of direction is known. This may be done by drawing the distances to a suitable scale.

Example 10

B is on a bearing of 065° from A and 3 km from A. Use a scale of 1 cm to 1 km to show the relative positions of A and B.

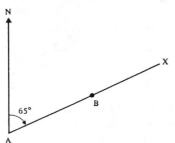

N

X

B

65°

A

Example 11

The first hole on a golf course is 280 m from the tee on a bearing of 090°.
On his first shot, a golfer drives the ball a distance of 160 m on a bearing of 060°.
Make a scale drawing to find the distance and bearing he should aim his next shot at the hole.
Use a scale of 1 cm to 40 m.

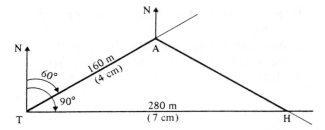

1 Draw a vertical line through T to fix North.
2 With your protractor, draw NT̂H at 90° in the clockwise direction from NT.
   Mark off point H 7 cm along this line TH: the distance from tee to hole is
   $280 \div 40 = 7$ cm.
3 Again with your protractor, draw NT̂A at 60° in the clockwise direction from NT.
   Mark off the point A 4 cm along this line TA: the ball travels $160 \div 40 = 4$ cm on the first shot.
4 Draw a vertical line NA through A to represent North.
   Then join the line AH.
5 Measure the length of AH and the size of the clockwise angle NÂH. AH = 4 cm, so the distance is $4 \times 40 = 160$ m.
   NÂH = 120°, so the bearing is 120°.

Exercise 6.12

1 On the sports field Jill threw the discus a distance of 35 m on a bearing of 060°. Belinda threw the discus a distance of 40 m on a bearing of 090°.

Make a scale drawing to find the distance and bearing of Belinda's discus from Jill's. Use a scale of 1 cm to 5 m.

2 There are three jetties A, B and C on a boating lake. B is 50 m due North of A; C is 50 m due East of A.

Use a scale drawing of 1 cm to 5 m to find the distance and bearing of C from B.

3 Sheffield is 100 km from Liverpool on a bearing of 090°. Stoke-on-Trent is 70 km from from Liverpool on a bearing of 135°.
   By drawing a map to a scale of 1 cm to 10 km, find the distance and bearing of Sheffield from Stoke-on-Trent.

4 Norwich is 200 km from Birmingham on a bearing of 090°. Oxford is 100 km from Birmingham on a bearing of 150°.
   Draw the relative positions of these cities to a scale of 1 cm to 25 km and hence find the distance and bearing of Norwich from Oxford.

5 Bristol is 200 km due South of Liverpool and Peterborough is 200 km from Liverpool on a bearing of 120°.
   Make a drawing to a scale of 1 cm to 25 km and from your drawing find the distance and bearing of Bristol from Peterborough.

6 In a cricket match the bowler is 20 m from the batsman on a bearing of 180°. The batsman hits the ball to a fielder 17.5 m away on a bearing of 150°. The fielder catches the ball and throws it back to the bowler.

Find from a scale drawing the distance and bearing for the fielder to throw the ball back. Use a scale of 1 cm to 2 m.

Angle properties

Adjacent angles are angles that are next to each other.

a 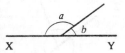 **b**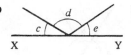

If XY is a straight line, then

a the adjacent angles $\hat{a}$ and $\hat{b}$ add up to 180°
  i.e. $\hat{a} + \hat{b} = 180°$

b the adjacent angles $\hat{c}$, $\hat{d}$, and $\hat{e}$ add up to 180°.
  i.e. $\hat{c} + \hat{d} + \hat{e} = 180°$

9 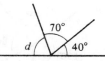 **10**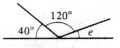

The sum of the angles at a point is 360°.

i.e. in the diagram
$\hat{a} + \hat{b} + \hat{c} = 360°$

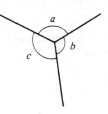

Example 12

a   **b**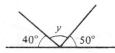

Find the size of $\hat{x}$.
$\hat{x} = 180° - 115°$
  $= 65°$

Find the size of $\hat{y}$.
$\hat{y} = 180° - 40° - 50°$
  $= 140° - 50°$
  $= 90°$

Example 13

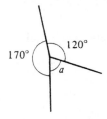

Find the size of $\hat{a}$.
$\hat{a} = 360° - 170° - 120°$
  $= 190° - 120°$
  $= 70°$

Exercise 6.13

For each question, find the size of the lettered angle.

1 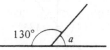 **2**

3 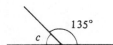 **4**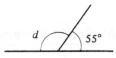

5 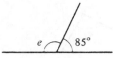 **6**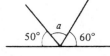

7 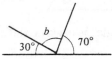 **8**

Exercise 6.14

For each question, find the size of the lettered angle.

1   **2**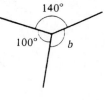

3 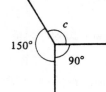 **4**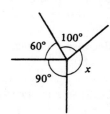

5 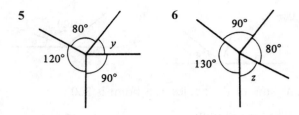 **6**

Two straight lines cross to form four angles, $\widehat{a}$, $\widehat{b}$, $\widehat{c}$ and $\widehat{d}$.

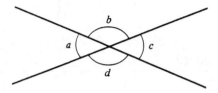

Two pairs of angles are equal.

$$\widehat{a} = \widehat{c}$$

$$\widehat{b} = \widehat{d}$$

The pairs of equal angles are known as *vertically opposite* angles.

Example 14

Find the size of $\widehat{a}$, $\widehat{b}$, $\widehat{c}$ formed by the two straight lines in the diagram.

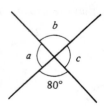

a Because $\widehat{a}$ and 80° are adjacent angles,
$\widehat{a} = 180° - 80° = 100°$

b Because $\widehat{b}$ is vertically opposite to 80°
$\widehat{b} = 80°$

c Because $\widehat{c}$ is vertically opposite to $\widehat{a}$
$\widehat{c} = 100°$

Exercise 6.15

Find the lettered angles formed by the straight lines in each diagram.

1 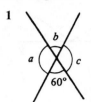 **2**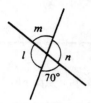

3 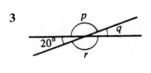 **4**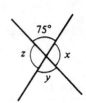

5 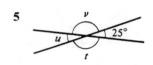 **6**

7 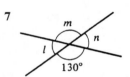 **8**

9 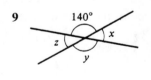 **10**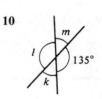

Angles in a triangle

A triangle has three sides that form three angles.

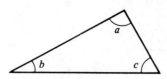

The sum of these three angles is always 180°.
i.e. $\widehat{a} + \widehat{b} + \widehat{c} = 180°$

There are three main types of triangle.

1 An acute-angled triangle: all its angles are less than 90°

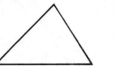

2 A right-angled triangle: its largest angle equals 90°

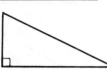

3 An obtuse-angled triangle: its largest angle is greater than 90°

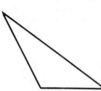

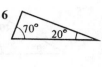

To find some unknown angles, you will need to use the angle properties of triangles, and also those of straight lines.

Example 15

Find the unknown angle in the following triangles and state the types of triangle.

a

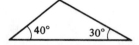

The unknown angle is 180° − 40° − 30°
= 140° − 30°
= 110°

The triangle is obtuse-angled.

b

The unknown angle is 180° − 50° − 60°
= 130° − 60°
= 70°

The triangle is acute-angled.

Exercise 6.16

Find the unknown angle in each triangle and state the type of triangle.

1 **2** **3**

Example 16

Find $\widehat{a}$, $\widehat{b}$ in the diagram.

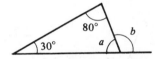

a The sum of the angles in a triangle is 180°
So $\widehat{a} = 180° − 80° − 30°$
$= 100° − 30°$
$= 70°$

b $\widehat{a}$ and $\widehat{b}$ are adjacent angles on a straight line.
So $\widehat{b} = 180° − \widehat{a}$
$= 180° − 70°$
$= 110°$

Exercise 6.17

Find the lettered angles in each of the following.

1  **2**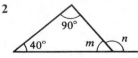

3 **4**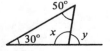

68

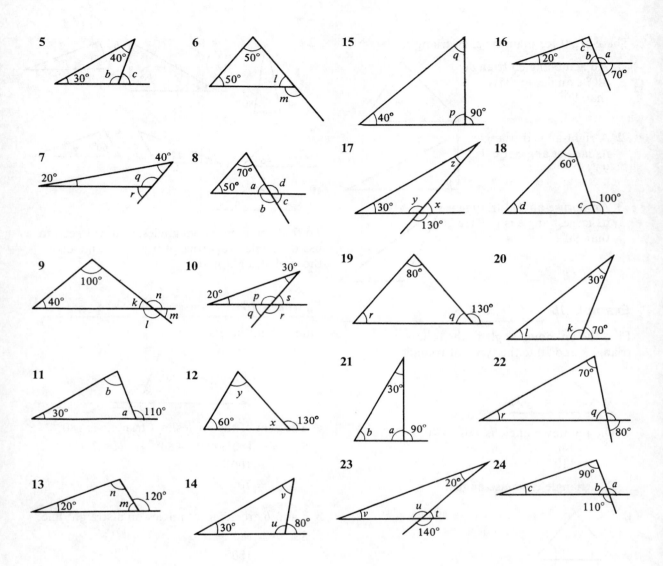

Unit 7 Probability

Fair decisions

Often, there are several possible outcomes in a given situation.

For example, each day somebody might decide whether to wear red or blue socks.

If the choice is made at *random*, we mean that it is done without deliberately trying to select any particular colour.

If each colour is *equally likely to be selected*, we say the choice is *fair*.

Example 1

Ali wants to decide whether to wear red or blue socks.

Are the following fair or unfair ways of deciding?

a Look out of the window. If it is raining wear red socks; if it is not raining wear blue socks.

b Put two socks in a bag, one of each colour. Choose one sock from the bag without looking and wear that colour.

c Select a word at random from the newspaper. If the word contains a letter 'z' wear red socks, if not wear blue.

a This is not a fair way of deciding because it is not raining for far more of the time than it is raining, even in Britain.

b This is a fair way of deciding because he is just as likely to pick a red sock as a blue one.

c This is not a fair way of deciding because there are far more words which do not contain a 'z' than words which do.

1 Bill and Wendy both hate doing the washing up.

They consider various ways to decide who will wash up on a particular day.

Are the following fair or unfair ways of deciding?
a Toss a coin. If it's heads, Bill washes up.
b If the day of the week contains a letter 'n', Bill washes up.
c If the month of the year contains a letter 'r', Wendy washes up.
d If there are leaves on the pear tree in the garden, Bill washes up.
e Both cut a deck of cards. If she gets the highest card, Wendy washes up.
f The tallest person does the washing up.
g The person with the longest name does the washing up.
h Both guess what colour the next car to drive up the street will be. The first person to be right does not have to wash up.

2 Salima and Lucy are on a train. They are trying to decide who will have the last sweet.

Are the following fair or unfair ways of deciding?
a The person who bought the sweets eats the last one.

b Lucy puts the sweet in one hand behind her back. Salima picks a hand, if the sweet is in it she eats it.

c They look out of the window. The first person to spot a horse in a field eats the sweet.

d They ask each other general knowledge questions. The first person who gets a question wrong loses and the other person eats the sweet.

e The person who has the biggest shoe size eats the sweet.

f They wait for the ticket collector to come. The person he speaks to first eats the sweet.

g They put their names on two pieces of paper, put them in a bag and then pick one out without looking.

h They check their pockets. The person with the largest number of 10 p coins eats the sweet.

3 John, Nilesh and Gavin all want to watch different TV programmes.
Are the following fair or unfair ways of deciding who chooses the programme?

a They all roll two dice. The person with the highest score chooses the programme.

b On the word 'go', they all hold up either an odd or an even number of fingers. They repeat this until there is an 'odd one out'. He chooses the programme they watch.

c They all go for a race around the block. The first one back chooses the programme they watch.

d They go out into the garden. The first one to find a worm chooses the programme they watch.

e They all play a computer game. The person with the highest score chooses the programme they watch.

f They ask somebody else to think of a number between 1 and 10. They take turns to guess the number and the first person to guess correctly chooses the programme they watch.

4 A teacher has to pick two pupils from her class of thirty each day to pick up litter.
Are the following fair or unfair ways of picking the pupils?

a The teacher picks the first two pupils on the class register.

b The teacher writes all the pupils' names on slips of paper, puts them in a box and then chooses two at random.

c The teacher picks the two pupils who came bottom in the last maths test.

d The teacher closes her eyes, waves a pin over the class register, then sticks it in twice to pick two names.

e The teacher picks the last two pupils that she saw dropping litter.

f The teacher gives all the pupils a number from 1 to 30. She then rolls five dice, adds the scores and selects the pupil with that number. She repeats this to select the other pupil.

g The teacher obtains 28 normal drinking straws and two straws with a drop of red paint on one end. She puts them in a cup so that it is impossible to see which ones have red paint on them. Each pupil then picks a straw and the ones who pick the straws with red paint pick up litter.

h The teacher picks the last two pupils to arrive in the classroom.

5 Daniel and Tom are lost. They have come to a crossroads and don't know whether to turn left, turn right or go straight on.

Are the following fair or unfair ways of deciding?

a Throw a pointed stick in the air and then go in whichever direction it points when it lands.

b Toss a coin first to decide between left and right. Then, having selected left or right, toss a coin again to decide between this direction and straight on.

c Daniel shuts his eyes and points with one arm. Tom spins him round and round. They go in whichever direction Daniel is pointing when he stops spinning.

d Go in the direction which will require the smallest turn of the handlebars.

e Write 'left', 'straight on' and 'right' on three pieces of paper. Put them in a pocket and select one at random.

f Each choose a direction and call it out on the word 'now'. Repeat this until two different directions are selected. Go in the direction that is not selected.

g Toss a coin to decide who will choose. Whoever wins selects a direction.

Probability

If we are certain that selection is fair and all outcomes are equally likely, we can calculate the *probability* that a particular outcome will happen.

A referee tosses a coin to decide whether the red team or the blue team will kick off. The red team captain calls 'heads'.

What is the probability that the red team will kick off?

There are two possible outcomes, 'heads' or 'tails'. So, the probability that the red team kicks off is $\frac{1}{2}$.

Example 12

A card is picked from a normal pack (without jokers).
What is the probability that it is a red queen?

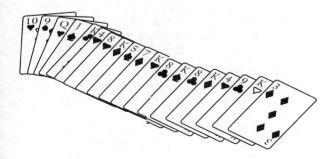

There are 52 cards in a pack and, of these, two are red queens. So the probability is

$$\frac{2}{52} = \frac{1}{26}$$

Example 3

A dice is rolled.
What is the probability that the score is

a a four?　**b** a factor of 6?　**c** a factor of 5?

a The probability is $\frac{1}{6}$

b There are four factors of 6 (1, 2, 3 and 6) so the probability is $\frac{4}{6} = \frac{2}{3}$

c There are two factors of 5 (1 and 5) so the probability is $\frac{2}{6} = \frac{1}{3}$

Exercise 7.2

1 If a letter is chosen at random from the word SUCCESS, what is the probability that it will be
a the letter S?　**b** the letter C?

2 If a letter is chosen at random from the word PEPPER, what is the probability that it will be
a the letter P?　**b** the letter E?

3 If a letter is chosen at random from the name GEORGE, what is the probability that it will be
a the letter E?　**b** the letter G?
c a vowel?　**d** a consonant?

4 If a letter is chosen at random from the name PENELOPE, what is the probability that it will be
a the letter E?　**b** the letter P?
c a vowel?　**d** a consonant?

5 If a letter is chosen at random from the word WOODWORK, what is the probability that it will be
a the letter O?　**b** the letter W?
c a consonant?

6 If a letter is chosen at random from the word NEEDLEWORK, what is the probability that it will be
a the letter E?　**b** a vowel?
c a consonant?

7 On a supermarket shelf there are 16 bags of sugar, 12 of which contain white sugar and 4 of which contain brown sugar.

If a bag is taken at random, what is the probability that it will contain
a white sugar? **b** brown sugar?

8 In class 3A there are 12 boys and 8 girls. If the pupils leave their classroom and walk to the assembly hall in any random order, what is the probability that the first pupil to enter the hall will be
a a boy? **b** a girl?

9 A farmer has 25 white sheep and 5 black sheep. If they are rounded up for shearing in any random order, what is the probability that the first one to be sheared will be
a white? **b** black?

10 A box of sweets contains 15 chocolates, 9 toffees and 6 nougats. If a sweet is taken from the box at random, what is the probability that it will be
a a chocolate? **b** a toffee? **c** a nougat?

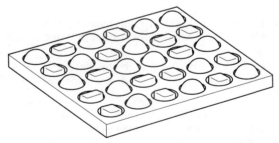

Probabilities can also be written as decimals or percentages.

Remember that any fraction can be changed into a decimal by dividing the top number by the bottom number.

Remember also that any decimal can be changed to a percentage by multiplying by 100.

Example 4

If a letter is chosen at random from the word SELECTED, what is the probability that it will be

a the letter S? **b** the letter E?
c neither an S nor an E?

Give each answer as a fraction, decimal and percentage.

a $\frac{1}{8} = 0.125 = 12.5\%$

b $\frac{3}{8} = 0.375 = 37.5\%$

c $\frac{4}{8} = \frac{1}{2} = 0.5 = 50\%$

Example 5

If a day of the week is selected at random, what is the probability that it will be

a Monday?
b a day which starts with a letter T?
c a day which is spelled with six letters?

Give each answer as a fraction, decimal and percentage.

a $\frac{1}{7}$, which is approximately 0.143 or 14.3%

b $\frac{2}{7}$, which is approximately 0.286 or 28.6%

c $\frac{3}{7}$, which is approximately 0.429 or 42.9%

Exercise 7.3

In questions **1** to **10**, give each answer as a fraction, decimal and percentage.

1 In class 2B there are 18 girls with dark hair, 10 girls with fair hair and 2 girls with red hair. If the teacher asks one girl at random to give out some books, what is the probability that she will have
a dark hair? **b** fair hair? **c** red hair?

2 A £1 cash bag contains six 10 p coins, four 5 p coins, six 2 p coins and eight 1 p coins. If a coin is removed from the bag, what is the probability that it will be
a a 10 p coin? **b** a 5 p coin?
c a 2 p coin? **d** a 1 p coin?
e a silver coin? **f** a copper coin?

3 On a supermarket shelf there are 8 packets of ready salted crisps, 5 packets of cheese and onion crisps, 3 packets of salt and vinegar crisps and 4 packets of prawn cocktail crisps.

If a bag is removed from the shelf at random, what is the probability that it will contain
  a ready salted crisps?
  b cheese and onion crisps?
  c salt and vinegar crisps?
  d prawn cocktail crisps?
  e any kind of flavoured crisps?

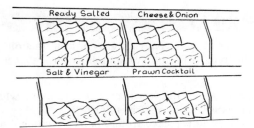

4 If a dice is thrown, what is the probability that the score will be
  a a six?   **b** an odd number?
  c an even number?   **d** a multiple of 3?
  e a prime number?   **f** a square number?
  g a triangle number?

5 Twelve counters numbered 1, 2, 3, 4, 5, 6, 7, 8, 9, 10, 11 and 12 are placed in a bag.

If a counter is removed from the bag, what is the probability that the number on it will be
  a a prime number?   **b** a square number?
  c a triangular number? **d** a multiple of 3?
  e a multiple of 5?

6 Twelve counters lettered A, B, C, D, E, F, G, H, I, J, K and L are placed in a bag.

If a counter is removed from the bag, what is the probability that the letter on it will be
  a a vowel?   **b** a consonant?
  c any letter of the word CAGE?
  d any letter of the word BLEACH?

7 Each month of the year is written on a card and the twelve cards are then placed in a bag.

If one card is then removed from the bag, what is the probability that
  a the first letter on the card is J?
  b the first letter on the card is M?
  c the first letter on the card is A?
  d the last letter on the card is R?
  e the last letter on the card is Y?
  f the month written on the card has 30 days?
  g the month written on the card has 31 days?

8 Certain geometrical shapes are drawn on cards as shown and the eight cards are then placed in a bag.

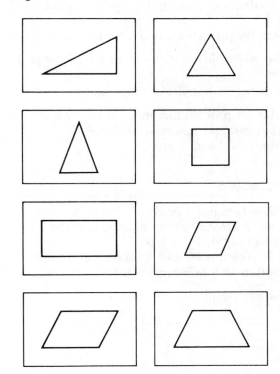

If a card is then removed from the bag, what is the probability that the figure on it has
  a three sides?   **b** four sides?
  c four equal sides?   **d** all its sides equal?
  e two pairs of equal sides?
  f one pair of equal sides?

9 A bag contains 40 counters, 8 of which are red, 12 of which are yellow, 4 of which are green and 16 of which are blue.

If a counter is removed from the bag, what is the probability that it is
  a red?   **b** yellow?   **c** green?   **d** blue?
  e red or yellow?   **f** red or green?
  g red or blue?

10 A pack of 52 playing cards is shuffled thoroughly and a card is then removed.

What is the probability that the card
  a is an ace?
  b is any king, queen or jack?
  c shows any number from 2 to 10?
  d shows any even number?
  e shows any odd number?

Number lines

If a bag contains 7 yellow counters the probability of picking out a yellow counter is $\frac{7}{7}$ or 1.
Thus the probability of a 'certainty' is 1.

The probability of picking out a red counter is $\frac{0}{7} = 0$.
Thus the probability of 'impossibility' is 0.

All other probabilities must be somewhere between 0 and 1; somewhere between 'impossible' and 'certain'.

Example 6

A case contains 3 pens and 5 pencils.
If one is selected at random, what is the probability that it is a pen?
Give your answer as a fraction and illustrate its position on a number line between 0 and 1.

The probability is $\frac{3}{8}$.

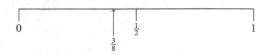

Example 7

A bag contains 3 strawberry and 2 lemon flavoured sweets.
If one is selected at random, what is the probability that it is strawberry flavoured?
Give your answer as a decimal and illustrate its position on a number line between 0 and 1.

The probability is $\frac{3}{5} = 0.6$

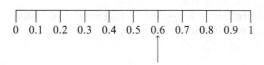

Example 8

In a packet, there are 3 chocolate biscuits and 7 plain biscuits.
If one is selected at random, what is the probability that it is plain?

Give your answer as a percentage and illustrate its position on a number line between 0 and 100%.

The probability is $\frac{7}{10}$ or 70%

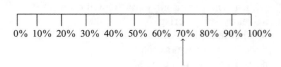

Exercise 7.4

In questions **1** to **5**, give your answer as a fraction and illustrate its position on a number line between 0 and 1.

1 If a season of the year is picked at random, what is the probability that it is Spring?
2 If one bead is picked from a bag containing 2 red, 3 blue and 3 green beads, what is the probability that it is red?
3 If a letter is chosen at random from the word SUCCESSFUL, what is the probability that it is the letter S?
4 If a normal pack of 52 cards is cut, what is the probability that the card is a diamond?
5 The National Lottery cards have numbers from 1 to 49.
   If a number is picked at random, what is the probability that it is the number 7?

In questions **6** to **10**, give your answer as a decimal and illustrate its position on a number line between 0 and 1.

6 There are one thousand possible combinations on a three-digit cycle lock.
   If you try 100 different combinations, what is the probability that you find the correct combination to open the lock?
7 In a raffle, 500 tickets are sold.
   If Mr Chaudray has bought 25 tickets, what is the probability that he wins the first prize?
8 There are 14 girls and 11 boys in class 7E.
   If one pupil is selected at random, what is the probability that it is a girl?
9 There are 15 sweets in a bag and 5 of them are mints.
   What is the probability that a sweet picked at random is not a mint?
10 If a letter is chosen at random from the word SUCCESSFUL, what is the probability that it is the letter C?

In questions **11** to **16**, give your answer as a percentage and illustrate its position on a number line between 0 and 100%.

11 A dice is made from a regular tetrahedron, with faces numbered from 1 to 4. The score is taken as the number on the bottom face.

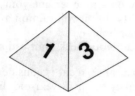

What is the probability that when the dice is rolled the score will be a prime number?

12 A restaurant menu offers a choice of one vegetable from peas, carrots, parsnips, broccoli and sweet corn.
What is the probability that a vegetable picked at random is green?

13 If one letter is picked at random from the word DISASTER, what is the probability that it is a vowel?

14 If a day of the week is selected at random, what is the probability that it is not Saturday or Sunday?

15 There are 16 horses in a race, one of which is called 'Old Glory'.
If a gambler selects a horse at random, what is the probability that she selects Old Glory?

16 Of the 20 cartons of eggs on a shop shelf, 11 contain brown eggs.
If a carton is picked at random, what is the probability that it contains brown eggs?

Estimating probabilities

In many real-life situations, we cannot be certain that all possible outcomes are equally likely.

Example 9

A glass tumbler, an egg, a knife and a calculator are all dropped on the floor.

a Estimate the probability that each will break and illustrate your answers on a number line.

b How could you check your estimates?

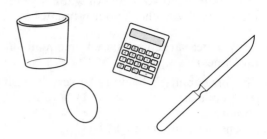

a We can estimate, using common sense, that the egg is almost certain to break, the glass will probably break, the calculator will probably not break and the knife will almost certainly not break.
We can show these estimates on a number line.

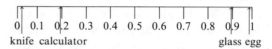

| 0 | 0.1 | 0.2 | 0.3 | 0.4 | 0.5 | 0.6 | 0.7 | 0.8 | 0.9 | 1 |

knife calculator   glass egg

b To check these estimates, we could conduct an experiment, perhaps dropping 100 eggs, 100 glasses, 100 calculators and 100 knives to see how many broke.

There are three ways to establish a probability.

1 By logical argument if we are certain that all outcomes are equally likely.
2 By using existing data, for example, school registers or weather records.
3 By conducting a survey or experiment.

Example 10

a What is the probability of scoring 1 when a dice is rolled?
b Estimate the probability that a Year 11 pupil picked at random in your school will have had 100% attendance since Year 7.
How could you check your estimate?
c Estimate the probability that when a slice of buttered bread is dropped it lands butter side up.
How could you check your estimate?

d Estimate the probability that a pupil selected at random from your school will like chips. How would you check your estimate?

a $\frac{1}{6}$ (by logical argument based on equally likely outcomes)

b This probability is likely to be very low, since few pupils attend until Year 11 with no absences.
A sensible estimate might be $\frac{1}{100}$.
The estimate could be checked by using existing data, in this case the school registers.

c This probability is likely to be close to $\frac{1}{2}$.
The estimate could be checked by an experiment, perhaps dropping a buttered slice of bread 100 times.

d This probability is likely to be very high, because chips are a very popular food.
A sensible estimate might be $\frac{19}{20}$ or even $\frac{99}{100}$.
The estimate could be checked by conducting a survey of perhaps 100 pupils selected at random.

Exercise 7.5

1 A drawing pin is dropped on a table.
  a Illustrate on a number line your estimate of the probability that it will land point up.
  b How could you check your estimate?

2 This chair falls off a table where it has been placed while the floor is swept.

  a Illustrate on a number line your estimate of the probability that it will *not* land on all four legs.

b Illustrate on the same line your estimate of the probability that it will land balanced on one leg.
  c How could you check your estimates?

3 Chantelle has planned a week's holiday in England in July.
  a Illustrate on a number line your estimate of the probability that it will rain on at least one day during her holiday.
  b How could you check your estimate?

4 A motor insurance agent is considering offering a one-year policy to an 18-year-old driver.
  a Illustrate on a number line your estimate of the probability that the driver will have an accident during the year.
  b How could you check your estimate?

5 A pupil is selected at random from your school.
  a Illustrate on a number line your estimate of the probability that the pupil will be a Manchester United supporter.
  b How could you check you estimate?

6 A pupil is selected at random from your school.
  a Illustrate on a number line your estimate of the probability that the pupil will eat school dinners.
  b How could you check your estimate?

7 A pupil is selected at random from your school.
  a Illustrate on a number line your estimate of the probability that the pupil will be in Year 7, Year 8 or Year 9.
  b How could you check your estimate?

8 Drashma buys £1000 worth of Premium Bonds.
  a Illustrate on a number line your estimate of the probability that she will win at least one prize in the first year she owns the bonds.
  b How could you check your estimate?

9 Tom tosses 4 coins.
  a Illustrate on a number line your estimate of the probability that the coins land as four heads.
  b How could you check your estimate?

10 A hand of five cards is dealt from the top of a normal pack of cards.
  a Illustrate on a number line your estimate of the probability that the hand contains at least one picture card.
  b How could you check your estimate?

Pie charts

A *pie chart* is a way of illustrating information. A circle is divided into sectors so that each separate sector represents a particular piece of information.

Example 1

A vending machine dispenses the following numbers of drinks on one day.

tea	coffee	hot chocolate	soup	milk	squash
108	84	36	60	24	48

Draw a pie chart to illustrate the number of drinks dispensed.

So the circle has to be divided into 360 equal parts, one part for each drink sold.

There are 360° in a circle, so an angle of 1° at the centre represents 1 drink.

The total number of drinks dispensed is

$$180 + 84 + 36 + 60 + 24 + 48 = 360$$

The sector angles are therefore as follows.

type of drink	tea	coffee	hot chocolate	soup	milk	squash
sector angle	108°	84°	36°	60°	24°	48°

The pie chart is then drawn as shown, using a protractor to mark off the angles.

Drinks dispensed from vending machine

Exercise 8.1

1 There are 240 girls in Year 10 at Oak Vale School. The pie chart shows how they chose from five sports options.
Find how many girls chose each of the five sports.

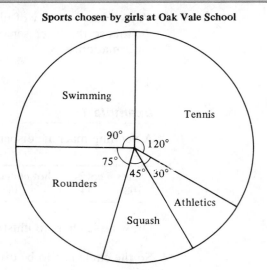

Sports chosen by girls at Oak Vale School

2 There are 180 boys in Year 11 at Grovehill School. The pie chart shows how they chose from four sports options.
Find how many boys chose each of the four sports.

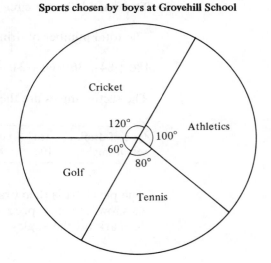

Sports chosen by boys at Grovehill School

In questions **3** to **8**, display the information on a pie chart.

3 One day a cafe sold 360 sandwiches. The list below shows how many of the various kinds.

60	cheese	30	tuna	45	tomato
90	egg	60	chicken	75	salad

4 In the village of Burwarton there are 360 people on the voting list. At one election they voted as follows.

150	Conservative	60	Liberal Democrat
120	Labour	30	did not vote

5 There are 360 pupils at Highfield School and they go to school by the following means.

      135   pupils walk to school
      120   pupils travel by bus
       75   pupils travel by train
       30   pupils cycle to school

6 One day a baker sells 180 loaves of bread. The list below shows how many loaves of each kind.

    75 large white   40 small white
    45 large brown   20 small brown

7 There are 120 boys at North Park School and the list below shows how many boys there are in each of the five classes.

    Class 1   30   Class 3 16   Class 5 30
    Class 2   24   Class 4 20

8 During the course of a week a hotel waitress received £24 in tips. The list below shows how much she received on each of the days that she worked.

    Monday £2   Wednesday £6   Friday   £8
    Tuesday £3   Thursday   £1   Saturday £4

9 A dice is thrown 30 times. The pie chart shows how frequently each of the scores occurred.
Find the number of times that each of the six scores occurred.

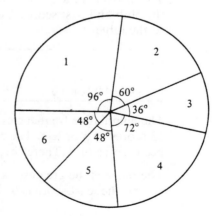

10. At Birmingham Station 240 people board a train which calls at Worcester, Cheltenham, Gloucester, Bristol and Weston-super-Mare. The number travelling to each of the five stations is shown in the list below.

    Worcester   30
    Cheltenham   50
    Gloucester   40
    Bristol   100
    Weston-super-Mare   20

Display these details on a pie chart.

Frequency tables

One hundred pupils take a Mathematics test marked out of 10. These are their scores.

0	0	1	1	1	1	1	2	2	2
2	2	2	2	2	2	3	3	3	3
3	3	3	3	3	3	3	3	3	4
4	4	4	4	4	4	4	4	4	5
5	5	5	5	5	5	5	5	5	5
5	5	5	6	6	6	6	6	6	6
6	6	6	6	6	6	6	6	6	7
7	7	7	7	7	7	7	7	8	8
8	8	8	8	8	8	9	9	9	9
9	9	9	9	10	10	10	10	10	10

A distribution of scores like this can be displayed in a *frequency table*.

score	0	1	2	3	4	5	6	7	8	9	10
frequency	2	5	9	13	10	14	16	9	8	8	6

The mode, median and the range can be found from the frequency table without using the original list of scores.

The *mode* is the most frequent score and we can see from the table that the mode is 6, because it is the score with the highest frequency.

The *median* is the middle score, which in a list of 100 scores will be between the 50th and 51st scores. To find the median we add cumulative frequencies to the table.

score	0	1	2	3	4	5	6	7	8	9	10
frequency	2	5	9	13	10	14	16	9	8	8	6
cumulative frequency	2	7	16	29	39	53	69	78	86	94	100

The cumulative frequencies show that there were 39 scores of 4 or less and 53 scores of 5 or less. The 50th and 51st scores must therefore have both been scores of 5. Therefore, the median is 5.

The *range* is the greatest value minus the least value. The greatest score is 10 and the least score is 0. Therefore the range is 10.

Example 2

This table shows the number of children per family in 100 families.

number of children	0	1	2	3	4	5	6
frequency	12	14	37	18	9	6	4

a Find the mode of the distribution.
b Find the median of the distribution.
c Find the range of the distribution.

a The mode is 2 children per family

b Adding cumulative frequencies to the table we have

number of children	0	1	2	3	4	5	6
frequency	12	14	37	18	9	6	4
cumulative frequency	12	26	63	81	90	96	100

In a distribution of 100 values the median will be between the 50th and 51st values.

The cumulative frequencies show that there were 26 families with 1 child or fewer and 63 families with 2 children or fewer. The 50th and 51st families must both have had 2 children.

Therefore the median = 2 children per family.

c The range of the distribution = $6 - 0 = 6$

Exercise 8.2

a Find the mode, median and range of each distribution.

b Illustrate each distribution with a pie chart.

1 The table below shows the times in which a 400-metre runner completed twenty races.

time (seconds)	55	56	57	58	59
frequency (no. of races)	1	4	7	5	3

2 The table below shows the weights of each of the thirty children in a class.

weight (kg)	40	41	42	43	44	45	46
frequency	2	3	5	8	7	4	1

3 The table below shows how many passengers a taxi driver carries after answering each of the thirty calls he received on a certain day.

number of passengers	1	2	3	4	5	6
frequency (no. of calls)	5	6	7	5	4	3

4 The table below shows how many wickets a bowler took in each match of a twenty-match season.

number of wickets	0	1	2	3	4	5	6
frequency (no. of matches)	1	2	3	5	6	3	0

5 The table below shows how many centuries a batsman scored in each season of his playing career.

number of centuries	0	1	2	3	4	5	6
frequency (no. of seasons)	0	3	4	5	2	1	0

The *mean* average can also be found directly from a frequency table.

This table shows the scores of a group of pupils in a mathematics test.

score (S)	0	1	2	3	4	5	6	7	8	9	10
frequency (F)	2	5	9	13	10	14	16	9	8	8	6

To find the mean we first add a line to the table recording each score multiplied by its frequency.

score (S)	0	1	2	3	4	5	6	7	8	9	10
frequency (F)	2	5	9	13	10	14	16	9	8	8	6
$S \times F$	0	5	18	39	40	70	96	63	64	72	60

Adding all the numbers in the frequency line tells us how many scores there were.

Adding all the products in the score $\times$ frequency line gives us the total of all the scores.

												Total
score (S)	0	1	2	3	4	5	6	7	8	9	10	
frequency (F)	2	5	9	13	10	14	16	9	8	8	6	100
$S \times F$	0	5	18	39	40	70	96	63	64	72	60	527

The mean is equal to the total of all the scores divided by the number of scores.

Therefore the mean = $527 \div 100 = 5.27$

Example 3

This table shows the number of children per family in 100 families.

number of children (N)	0	1	2	3	4	5	6
frequency (F)	12	14	37	18	9	6	4

Find the mean number of children.

								Total
number of children (N)	0	1	2	3	4	5	6	
frequency (F)	12	14	37	18	9	6	4	100
$N \times F$	0	14	74	54	36	30	24	232

Mean = $232 \div 100 = 2.32$

Exercise 8.3

Find the mean of each distribution.

1 The table below shows how many goals a hockey player scored in each of the matches that she played during a certain season.

number of goals	0	1	2	3	4	5
frequency (no. of matches)	8	13	10	6	2	1

2 The table below shows the finishing positions over twenty seasons for a rugby club which plays in a ten-club league.

position	1st	2nd	3rd	4th	5th	6th	7th	8th	9th
frequency (no. of seasons)	0	1	1	2	5	7	3	1	0

3 The table below shows how many school lunches were taken by the children in class 2B on each day of a sixty-day term.

number of lunches taken	1	2	3	4	5	6	7	8	9	10	11
frequency (no. of days)	0	1	4	5	7	8	10	11	8	3	3

4 Kelly travelled to school by bus on each day of a sixty-day term. The table below shows the times that each bus journey took.

time (minutes)	30	31	32	33	34	35
frequency (no. of journeys)	5	8	10	16	14	7

5 The table below shows how many pupils in Class 1B were absent on each day of a sixty-day term.

number absent	0	1	2	3	4	5	6
frequency (no. of days)	10	15	20	6	5	2	2

Exercise 8.4

1 Find the mode, median, mean and range of the distribution.
A small hotel has accommodation for ten overnight guests and is open during June, July, August and September. The table below shows how many guests stayed on each night of an opening season.

number of guests	0	1	2	3	4	5	6	7	8	9	10
frequency (no. of nights)	5	10	12	15	20	16	15	10	8	6	5

2 Find the mode, median, mean and range of the distribution.
At Westfield School the pupils are told their examination marks rounded to the nearest ten. The table below shows the marks of one hundred Year 10 pupils in a mathematics examination.

mark	0	10	20	30	40	50	60	70	80	90	100
frequency (no. of pupils)	0	2	5	15	18	20	15	12	10	3	0

3 The table below shows how many international caps a footballer earned in each season of his international career.

1967	1	1971	3	1975	3	1979	2	1968	2
1972	5	1976	4	1980	2	1969	3	1973	6
1977	3	1981	3	1970	4	1974	4	1978	5

a Copy and complete the tally chart below.

number of caps per season	tally	frequency
1	/	1
2		
3		
4		
5		
6		

b Copy the frequency distribution table below and use your tally chart to complete it.

no. of caps per season	1	2	3	4	5	6
frequency						

c Find the mode, median, mean and range of the distribution.

4 The table below shows how many bottles of milk a milkman delivered to each of the forty houses in South Street.

Number 1.	2	Number 15.	3	Number 29.	6
Number 2.	3	Number 16.	3	Number 30.	1
Number 3.	4	Number 17.	2	Number 31.	3
Number 4.	1	Number 18.	1	Number 32.	4
Number 5.	5	Number 19.	3	Number 33.	6
Number 6.	3	Number 20.	2	Number 34.	2
Number 7.	2	Number 21.	2	Number 35.	4
Number 8.	3	Number 22.	1	Number 36.	5
Number 9.	4	Number 23.	3	Number 37.	3
Number 10.	2	Number 24.	3	Number 38.	1
Number 11.	3	Number 25.	4	Number 39.	4
Number 12.	1	Number 26.	2	Number 40.	2
Number 13.	4	Number 27.	4		
Number 14.	2	Number 28.	5		

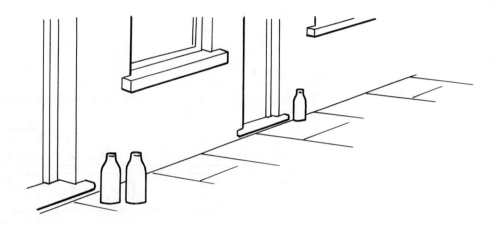

a Copy and complete the tally chart below.

number of bottles per house	tally	frequency
1	⊬⊬ /	6
2		
3		
4		
5		
6		

b Copy the frequency distribution table below and use your tally chart to complete it.

no. of bottles per house.	1	2	3	4	5	6
frequency						

c Find the mode, median, mean and range of the distribution.

5 The table below shows the outside temperature (°C) in Stourbridge for each day of January in 1991.

Tue	1st	5°	Tue	8th	1°	Tue	15th	3°	Tue	22nd	5°	Tue	29th	6°
Wed	2nd	6°	Wed	9th	0°	Wed	16th	3°	Wed	23rd	5°	Wed	30th	6°
Thur	3rd	5°	Thur	10th	0°	Thur	17th	4°	Thur	24th	4°	Thur	31st	4°
Fri	4th	4°	Fri	11th	1°	Fri	18th	4°	Fri	25th	6°			
Sat	5th	3°	Sat	12th	1°	Sat	19th	3°	Sat	26th	5°			
Sun	6th	3°	Sun	13th	2°	Sun	20th	4°	Sun	27th	4°			
Mon	7th	2°	Mon	14th	2°	Mon	21st	4°	Mon	28th	5°			

a Make a tally chart to show this information.
Copy the table below and use your tally chart to complete it.

temperature	0°	1°	2°	3°	4°	5°	6°
frequency (no. of days)							

b Find the mode, median, mean and range of the distribution.

Example 4

1 The numbers of children in 80 households in two different areas of a town were recorded.

number of children	0	1	2	3	4	5	6
frequency (area X)	12	13	28	22	3	1	1

number of children	0	1	2	3	4	5	6
frequency (area Y)	42	23	15	0	0	0	0

a Find the mode, median, mean and range of each distribution.
b Draw bar charts to illustrate each distribution.
c Compare and comment on the two distributions.

a For area X

$$\text{mode} = 2 \text{ children}$$

$$\text{median} = 2 \text{ children}$$

$$\text{mean} = \frac{158}{80} = 2.0 \text{ children (to 1 dp)}$$

$$\text{range} = 6 - 0 = 6 \text{ children}$$

For area Y

$$\text{mode} = 1 \text{ child}$$

$$\text{median} = 0 \text{ children}$$

$$\text{mean} = \frac{53}{80} = 1.0 \text{ child (to 1 dp)}$$

$$\text{range} = 2 - 0 = 2 \text{ children}$$

b

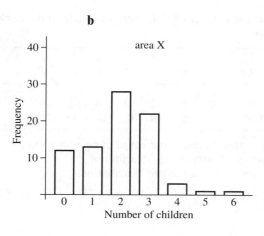

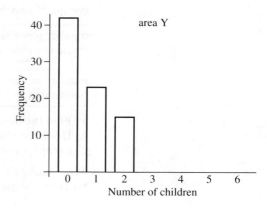

c All the averages indicate that there are far fewer children living in households in area Y than there are in area X.

The number of children per household is smaller in area Y with a range of 2 to 0 children whereas area X has a range of 6 to 0 children.

The bar charts illustrate these differences.

Exercise 8.5

1 These tables show the number of tests taken by the students at two driving schools before they passed.

number of tests	1	2	3	4	5
frequency (school M)	28	12	5	3	2

number of tests	1	2	3	4	5
frequency (school N)	45	30	21	4	0

a Find the mode, median, mean and range of each distribution.
b Draw bar charts to illustrate each distribution.
c Compare and comment on the two distributions.

2 These tables show the number of visits per year made to the doctor by two groups of patients.

number of visits	0	1	2	3	4	5	6	7	8	9	10
frequency (group A)	15	20	25	15	10	6	5	3	1	0	0

number of visits	0	1	2	3	4	5	6	7	8	9	10
frequency (group B)	2	6	10	12	20	30	50	40	20	6	4

a Find the mode, median, mean and range of each distribution.
b Draw bar charts to illustrate each distribution.
c Compare and comment on the two distributions.

3 These tables show the number of matches per box in samples of two different types of match.

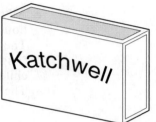

number of matches per box	37	38	39	40	41	42	43	44	45
frequency (striko)		8	18	23	31	27	11	13	4	6

number of matches per box	37	38	39	40	41	42	43	44	45
frequency (katchwell)		0	27	45	39	21	0	0	0	0

a Find the mode, median, mean and range of each distribution.
b Draw bar charts to illustrate each distribution.
c Compare and comment on the two distributions.